RICHEST
ENGINEER

THE
RICHEST
ENGINEER

A Story That Will Unravel The Secrets Of The Rich

ABHISHEK KUMAR

Sarvatra
An imprint of Manjul Publishing House

First published in India by

Sarvatra
An imprint of Manjul Publishing House

◆2nd Floor, Usha Preet Complex, 42 Malviya Nagar, Bhopal 462 003 - India
◆7/32, Ground Floor, Ansari Road, Daryaganj, New Delhi 110 002 - India
Website: www.manjulindia.com

This edition first published in 2016

ISBN   978-93-81506-87-5

Cover image © Shutterstock

Printed and bound in India by Manipal Technologies Ltd., Manipal

Disclaimer
This book is not intended to provide personalised legal, accounting, financial or investment advice. Professional advice must be sought for matters such as interpretation of the law, proper accounting procedures, financial planning, and investment strategies. The author and the publisher will not be liable in any manner for loss or risk which may be incurred as a direct or indirect consequence of the use and application of any of the contents of this work.

All characters and situations in this book are fictitious and any resemblance to any person or place is co-incidental. Although the author has exhaustively researched all sources to ensure accuracy and completeness of the information contained in this book, the author and the publisher assume no responsibility whatsoever for any errors, inaccuracies, omissions or inconsistencies in it. Readers are encouraged to bring to the notice of the author/publisher for any factual error which might have been missed by the author.

To My Family

CONTENTS

ACKNOWLEDGEMENTS

There is a woman at the beginning of all great things.
Alphonse De Lamartine (1790–1869)

This book would not have come into its existence without the love, support and belief of my wife, Rakshmi. Since the day I decided to write a book on personal finance, which will help people live a holistic and fulfilling life, she's encouraged me to follow my heart and passion to see that the book reaches the hand of every worthy individual who is eager to uplift his/her life. From the person who is not an avid reader to reviewing, editing and providing inputs for the book, she's stuck with me through good times and bad. Rakshmi, thank you for your patience and support – you're my rock. Also special thanks to my daughter Arshika, whose love and smile of every moment keeps me sane and lively each day.

I would also like to thank my parents for believing in me and encouraging me to follow my passion. A special thanks to my sister Mayuri and my brother-in-law Rahul Bhatia for reviewing the work and providing feedback.

A big thanks to my friends and colleagues who did the difficult task of proofreading my work. Arun Kumar, Pawan Singh, Rohit Vats...a big 'Thank You' to all of you.

Finally, I am deeply grateful to Kapil Singh, Editor, Manjul Publishing House, who understood my concept and idea along with the impact that it could have on people's lives. A huge thanks, also to the entire editorial and publishing team at Manjul, for their efforts to bring out this book in its present form. I would also like to offer my sincere thanks to the sales, marketing and publicity department of Manjul, who left no stone unturned in creating a brand for the book to make it available at all the leading bookshops across the country.

PREFACE

The wisest advice to develop and follow a financial plan is easy to understand...a schema that responds effectively to the questions and needs of the reader. Similarly, the most articulately expressed thoughts on personal finance may be most useful when they are presented in a style, which arouses and maintains the interest of the readers.

So how does one write an understandable and entertaining book on personal finance, which also answers the queries and doubts of its readers? Isn't finance a boring topic to discuss?

Possibly, a message conveyed through a story is grasped by the reader in the best possible way. Why is it so? It is because only when you relate to the characters from the story told that you learn the most.

This is the same philosophy I have used in presenting the lessons of personal finance through a 'work of fiction.' This book has been primarily written as a novel with a message and learning to be absorbed the reader from each and every line of the book.

Rather than inundating you with intimidating charts, graphs or a series of lifeless numbers, *The Richest Engineer* will entertain and inform you. The book takes a different route by presenting the messages through diagrams. After all, a picture is worth more than a thousand words.

Through the continuous conversation between Vinay, the financial hero and Ajay, his college friend, you will learn the *secrets of wealth creation and accumulation* – the secrets that has been preserved by the rich to be passed down only through generations. You will also learn that sound financial planning is not only simple, but it can also be fun.

I wish you a good and entertaining read. Enjoy the journey of Ajay with Vinay's help and guidance.

Abhishek Kumar

INTRODUCTION

I had the opportunity to get to know about the lives and habits of the rich. As part of my job description at Axis Bank, it was required to give a brief profile of each of the board of directors of the large corporates of India. All these people are very learned and experienced in their profession. Also, almost all of them are among the Richest Club of the Country. So just for the curiosity, I delved more into the lives and habits of the Directors of the Large Companies of India than was required for my job. I started reading about their upbringing, their education, their lifestyle and everything about them that I could lay my hands upon. And what did I learn? I learnt a lot.

It was an interesting observation to conclude that almost all the rich people share similar traits when it comes to money. Most of them have a specific way of thinking, acting and behaving when it comes to money. So, after two years research, it was found that there were few basic principles, which were followed by all of them. After research, I found that if anyone follows these principles, they inevitably succeed – become rich! Everybody can become a millionaire when they just follow the habits of the rich. I also learnt a fat pay cheque was hardly the prerequisite to become rich. Just to give you comfort; here is a secret revealed in my study on the directors of the largest companies of India. I have found many started small and today they are among the elite club of the corporate India.

During my research I have also read several books by great authors, professors and motivational speakers. My efforts revealed the teachings that these great men preach about wealth building were already being followed by almost all the rich and successful people.

What I have presented in this book through the fictional characters of Ajay and Vinay is nothing new. Yes, I have not devised any new method of creating wealth and becoming rich. To say, I have found new ways to become rich is akin to the claim I have discovered new antiques. These principles are not mine. Rather, I have taken them from all the rich people. After all, there is nothing new under the sun. I have also taken the lessons put forth by great authors, professors and speakers and tried to incorporate them in the book giving due credit to the concerned authors, professors and speakers in the footnotes.

All the wisdom that I have presented here is being followed by the moneyed people since time immemorial. There is nothing new about these principles and wisdom, it just so happens that they have been kept underground by a few members of the society, who have passed them on only to their generations. No schools, colleges or universities have courses about the basics of personal finance and the principles or the clues to the wisdom of becoming wealthy, which every one of us deserves to be. And that is one of the basic reasons why rich become richer, poor become poorer and middle class struggle all throughout their lives because they have been taught differently about money.

Now, it is no more a secret. It is being presented to you. These principles are simple, effective and fairly easy to apply. They have been tested, proven over and over again. Surely they will work for you when you accept them enough to apply them in your own life. After all, they have worked for each and every one the rich and successful people .

So, all I expect from you is that you read it, understand it and practice it. Because without practicing, all the wisdom that you are going to learn from this book will go waste and instead of reading a great book to make your life prosper, you would end up reading just another novel.

Now, at this moment break the chain. Just rise to your full potential. Explore the endless opportunities that the world has to offer to you. It is all about living your dreams – this book will help you in your journey to be free to realise them.

Yet, before we begin there are few caveats that I would like to discuss. First, in no way do I mean to show disrespect to poor people or want to appear to be without compassion for their situation. I do not believe that rich people are better than poor people. They are rich just because they have aligned their habits conducive to wealth creation. At the same time, I want to make sure you get the message, so I am going to make the distinctions between rich and poor people *'as extreme as possible.'*

Second, I will be generalising *'big time.'* I understand that neither all rich, nor all poor people are the way I'm describing them to be. Again, my objective is to make sure you get the point of each principle to enable you to use it, hence their somewhat exaggerated depiction.

And third, I have used masculine gender in most of the

cases and examples, only for the purpose of ease in writing. The principles and wisdom apply to both genders.

Do read it. You can bask and glow under the wisdom of ages. It is for you to grab it. You are just 250 pages behind the 'enlightened' you.

Part I

THE THINKING

One

A SLEEPLESS NIGHT

Ajay woke up suddenly at 2AM in the night. He was breathing heavily with a few beads of sweat dripping down his forehead. He rushed to the bathroom to wash his face but catching sight of himself sweating profusely in the mirror terrified him further. After he washed his face and legs, wiped them with the towel, he crept into the bed without disturbing his wife and daughter. The fear of his home getting foreclosed and auctioned by the bank was giving him nightmares. He tried hard to get back to sleep, with thoughts that things will change. Surely, it will be a better tomorrow yet deep down in his heart he knew that he might lose his most precious asset, his home.

Ajay, after graduating from NIT Allahabad was working as a Lead Engineer in Bengaluru with an MNC software company with its headquarters in South Korea. His wife, Priya, too was employed as a Senior Software Engineer in one of the IT Consulting Companies in Bengaluru, itself. The two were married around four years ago. Both had progressed well in their careers. Their daughter, Kiara, was nearly ten months old. Ajay, a doting father was deeply fond of spending each weekend completely devoted to her.

It was a beautiful Sunday morning. The sun had risen over the horizon and its rays filtered through the leaves and twigs of the trees illuminated the residential complex, where Ajay had purchased a three bedroom flat to set up home after Kiara was born. The residential complex was one of the most sought after localities in Bengaluru due to its proximity to the nearby IT offices. The complex had all the essential amenities although these remained mostly unutilised either because of the busy work schedule of the residents or simply because of their lethargy.

After he got out of bed, Ajay went to the kitchen to make himself a cup of tea. As he hadn't had a good night's rest, he woke with a mild headache. While the tea was brewing, Ajay glanced at Priya who was in deep sleep holding Kiara with her left hand. Kiara too, was feeling blissfully cosy in the warmth of her mother's arms. She would smile abruptly for a moment, then would go back to sleep. Kiara's smile would melt Ajay's heart – he could stand still till eternity watching his daughter smile. Suddenly the overflowing tea from the saucepan brought his mind back to the kitchen and he silently poured a cup of tea for himself and went to the balcony to enjoy the freshness of the morning air.

Ajay was a bright student throughout his schooldays. His father, now retired, was a state government employee, who had worked diligently all his life towards the development under his charge in a village of Allahabad district. His mother, a homemaker, looked after the house and studies of her children. As the eldest of the three brothers, Ajay had the extra responsibility of looking after the family whenever his father was out of town on official visits.

'Look Son, you are the eldest among all your brothers. If you do well in your studies and your career, then all your brothers will do well. I am a government employee with not much resources to help you all study in private colleges as the fees there are extremely expensive. Even if I invest my entire life's savings, it would scarcely be able to pay fees for even one of you. It's my deepest desire that all three of you go to good colleges and universities to become well qualified for a successful career. Still I feel helpless when I think about the money that would be required to fund your college education.'

Ajay's father paused for some time trying to control his tears, then continued 'Our only hope is that you all get admitted to good government colleges that charge lesser fees, have better faculties and also offer better job prospects than private colleges. However, admission to government colleges would not be an easy task as there is stiff competition in the entrance exams. Nevertheless I have full faith in you. Actually I am pretty sure that you will do well to make us all proud.'

These words from his father were ingrained in Ajay's mind when he had just passed his standard nine exam and was about to enter standard ten.

Ajay's thoughts were broken as the doorbell rang. He went to the main door only to find the newspaper and milk packets hanging from the door's knob. After he put the milk in the refrigerator, he started browsing through the newspaper. Two of the headlines caught his attention in particular, 'Slowdown in the IT Sector – Companies looking to downsize operations' and 'Recessionary Trend in the Real Estate Market – Supply Outpacing Demand.' Ajay knew that he too was a victim of the above two developments. He was feeling helpless as he didn't know whom to consult or what should he do so that he can sort out his problems – his financial trouble.

After cracking the All India Engineering Entrance Examination, more commonly known as AIEEE, with a good rank, Ajay was able to get a seat in the Computer Science Department of NIT Allahabad. It was a dream-come-true for his entire family. Except for his father who had graduated from Allahabad University, none of his family members including the extended ones had made it so far.

Ajay still remembered his father, beaming with pride, while his younger brothers, who were still in school, were jumping with joy. 'You truly have made us proud, my son,' his father's words were still fresh in his memory. His mother was delighted that her son has done something good enough to bring laurels to the family.

Ajay graduated from NIT Allahabad with distinction as well as landed a coveted job in one of the top software companies. He moved to Bengaluru to start his career. After some initial hiccups, he started proving that he was worth his salt. He even got two of his ideas patented and was appreciated by his colleagues as well as his superiors. Many a time he had to go to South Korea, his company's head quarter; for short trips, to sort some issues or for integration of solutions, which were being developed jointly by the Indian team as well as their counterparts in Korea.

As time progressed, so did his career. From Software Engineer, he had graduated to Senior Software Engineer and then to Lead Engineer. At the personal front too he wasn't doing badly either. He had saved some money from his Korea trips. Before settling down with a family he had purchased a three bedroom apartment in a place nearby his office. He had made the requisite 20% down payment from his savings and for the balance 80% he had availed a home loan from a bank. At that time he had thought that he had bagged a good deal. He didn't know that he would repent later on.

After some time Ajay married Priya. Within three years, they had the most joyous moment of their life when they were blessed with Kiara. Relatives from both the sides had flocked to Bengaluru to wish the parents and to give blessings to their granddaughter. The grandparents were happier than the parents themselves. Of course they had plenty of advice about how to raise the little one. The things both of them needed to do for her as also some changes in their lifestyle to give proper attention to their princess.

Everything seemed to be going smoothly for them, until last week, when Ajay got the shock of his life. His manager informed him that his entire business unit was going to be shut down as the product on which they had been working for the past two years did not get the initially envisaged market response. The unit was making continuous losses – it was becoming difficult for the management to continue with this project. Consequently a mandate was issued to close the project along with the business unit working on it. His manager told him that he had two months to look outside for another job before the proverbial pink slip would be handed over to every individual in his unit.

'But Sir, I have been the most consistent performer of our team. My work was noticed by the Senior Management as well. They had even commended me in our Annual Meeting. How can they ask me to leave?' retorted Ajay.

'I understand your concern. Even I had put up your case to them but they didn't listen. They are saying that other business units are under performing and overstaffed as well. So chances of you fitting in other projects are very remote. I know you are a talented guy and you will definitely find something good for you,' consoled his manager.

Ajay had become teary-eyed thinking of the last week incident when suddenly Priya came to his side and put her head on his lap while he was lost in his thoughts sitting on his recliner holding the newspaper in his hand. He had already discussed his layoff with her and knew that Priya too was worried about their near future.

'How are we going to pay our EMI? We hardly have any money left that would support us for more than six months,' Ajay said meekly.

'There will be a way out. We don't need to worry. We have to keep calm enough to look for possible solutions,' said Priya as she got up.

'We have put all our savings as down payment for this apartment of ours. Now we don't have much. At the moment you have taken a sabbatical for a year. I don't know what will happen if I am not able to get another job in next two months,' Ajay was looking more worried now as he became tense.

'Taking a sabbatical was not my decision alone. We had taken that decision jointly as we had to raise Kiara. It was you who were against putting Kiara in a crèche or at the mercy of some maid. Even I didn't want that – so I took leave from the work. Now you are blaming me?'

'I am not blaming you,' Ajay softened his voice as he tried to pacify Priya. 'I am only concerned, how we will make our home loan EMI payments to the bank. We also have our car loan to take care of, as well. I cannot even ask my father for help as he is already funding college fees of my younger brothers and he doesn't have any surplus money to lend me.'

Priya made herself some tea. After ensuring that Kiara was still sleeping she went to take a seat in their new recliner sofa which they had purchased online using the EMI option provided by the e-commerce company.

'You know, I have got this weird feeling that we have been making mistakes. Mistakes that are costing us now,' said Priya taking a sip from her cup.

'What mistakes?'

'I think we have not been good in terms of handling our money. We have been too extravagant, too eager to splurge on everything. We took our job to be a permanent affair and thought our salary would always find its way into our account at the end of every month. We never did any financial planning and neither had we thought of taking steps in that direction. And now that both of our salaries seem to be going out of our sight, we are suddenly pressing the panic button.'

'But,' Ajay tried to interrupt her.

'There are no ifs and buts now. Don't you see that even when both of us were earning well, we fell in a trap ourselves?' Priya too was becoming worried now.

'I guess you are correct. Probably, we shouldn't have purchased this apartment itself. Then, this whole problem wouldn't have bothered us,' came the quick reply from Ajay.

'No, purchasing the apartment was not a wrong decision. The real estate prices have always been increasing. In any case. one day we would need our own home, the sooner we had the better it was for us.'

'Then what mistakes did we make which have led us into this trap,' Ajay was getting irritated now.

'I am not very sure. I guess the way we have looked at things, the way we have been living; the way we have been spending; all these don't seem to make sense to me now.'

'I am not getting what you are pointing to.'

'Why don't we go and meet your friend Vinay. I was thinking about the discussion we had when you told me that Vinay has been doing pretty well. After all both of you are school friends and know each other well. Probably, he can help us find some solution to our problem.'

Ajay's eye glistened on hearing Vinay's name. Both of them had done their schooling together and in fact they had graduated from the same college. While Ajay was always among the rank holders at the engineering institute, Vinay used to be somewhere in the range of average in the department's ranking table.

Ajay knew that Vinay was doing pretty well for himself despite getting lower salary than what he was earning. In fact, his father had also asked him to be in touch with Vinay. He too, had planned many times to meet Vinay but a busy work life meant these plans never materialised. Yet now the time was ripe for him to meet his old friend to seek his guidance. Surely he could learn from Vinay how to create wealth for himself, something, Ajay had not been able to do.

'Hello Vinay,' Ajay was speaking on the latest smart phone available in the market.

'Hey Ajay,' came the reply. 'How are you doing my friend? It's been so long since we met.'

'True, too long. Shall we meet next weekend? I have much to discuss with you.'

'I hope everything is fine at your end?' asked Vinay.

'Yes, everything is perfect. Just wanted to meet you to discuss something important. Hope, it wouldn't be much of a problem for you.'

'You are always welcome. I also planned to meet you. Good you called me. See you then this coming Saturday.'

Two

A DIFFERENT LESSON

Vinay and Ajay were childhood friends. Both of them lived in the same neighbourhood in Allahabad. While Ajay's father was a UP State Government employee, Vinay's father, Ram Prasad was a businessman; trading food grains and other agricultural products. He used to bring food grains such as wheat and maize from Punjab and Haryana to resell them in the local market.

Ram Prasad's father was a landless farmer in Dharampur, which is a small village in Allahabad district. After seeing the plight of his father and other landless farmers in his village, Ram Prasad had decided to move to the city to eke out his living. As a farmer's son, he knew the intricacies of growing food grains, times of the cultivation and harvest, hence he was well able to judge the quality of the food grains by merely a look at it. Though his knowledge of food grains helped him earlier in his business, it was his relationship with his suppliers and customers, which consolidated his position in the market.

He used to say to his son, 'In the market, nothing is more important than your reputation for absolute integrity and your goodwill. You should be perfectly honest in everything you do and in every transaction and activity. But creating a strong reputation and goodwill takes time and these come when you remain firm to your words. If you have given a commitment to your supplier that you would purchase certain material at a given price in future, then you should purchase those even if you think you would make a loss in that particular transaction. Similarly, if you have promised something to your customers then you should deliver those on time to them. It is these small losses that create bigger profits for you in the long run.'

Ram Prasad had a deep desire to create wealth for himself. He didn't want his children to suffer the way he had to suffer. He knew that his father had tried his best to provide for his family but he wanted to give more. He wanted better education for his children, bigger house for his family, better comfort and other fine things that life has to offer. He started working hard, brought in more food grains, hired some staff to handle the increased business but was not able to increase his income.

'If you want to learn to do something right, watch someone who has done it successfully. And if you do not get everything what you were seeking by observing and watching then go to that person and ask how he does it,' Ram Prasad had advised Vinay when he did not get the desired rank in AIEEE and was not able to get a seat in the college of his choice. The same principle Ram Prasad had used when his efforts were not bearing results. At the age of twenty-nine and after making multiple attempts to increase his wealth and business, he did what he used to call the best thing he had ever done in his life. He went to meet Seth Munshi Lal; the richest businessman in whole of Allahabad.

In his sixties, Seth Munshi Lal, popularly known as Sethji was widely respected in Allahabad. He owned two textile stores, three food grain mills, one petrol pump, extensive real estate and multiple vehicles, which he used to rent out on contract.

Seth Munshi Lal had always liked Ram Prasad. He admired him for his loyalty to his family while he was also impressed with Ram Prasad's honesty and his entrepreneurial approach to expand his business. So when Ram Prasad told Seth Munshi Lal why he had dropped by, Sethji nodded, 'You've come to the right place, my boy. I'll teach you the golden secret of financial success as I consider you to be worthy of this knowledge.'

After receiving the financial wisdom from Seth Munshi Lal, Ram Prasad started his journey towards his goal of accumulating wealth so that he could provide the best of comforts for his family. He also learnt about managing money during his course of work, which helped him further in his business. Having seen money come into his hand and then going out, he learnt certain rules of money, which governed its accumulation and subsequent growth. He started noting down these rules in his diary in which he had already scribed the financial wisdom which he had learnt from Seth Munshi Lal. He used to call these rules as '*Scrolls of Wealth Creation and Accumulation.*'

Vinay, like his father was hardworking. The failure to get the seat in the college of his choice didn't deter him from working hard. He didn't envy his friends who were able to make it through the engineering entrance exams; rather he went and congratulated them. And just like his father had advised him, he asked his friends how they were able to crack the exam; which books did they refer to and how they approached certain sections of the syllabus in which he had some difficulties. And no sooner than the year had passed, that Vinay told his parents about clearing the exam and bagging a seat in the Computer Science Department of NIT Allahabad.

Vinay used to visit home in every semester break. But this time it was different. It was the beginning of his seventh semester and he had come home with the job offer letter from one of the IT companies in Bengaluru. Everyone was happy at home and his parents in particular were beaming with joy. After all, their son had become an engineer. Once the party was over, Ram Prasad asked Vinay to come with him to enjoy some hot *jalebis* at the nearby *mithai* shop.

'Son, now that you are set to start your professional life and that you are going to earn money, I am going to tell you something, which I would like you to remember throughout your life,' his father told while walking with him.

Vinay attentively listened to his father.

'There are three types of learning that we get in our life. The first is the one that we get from our formal education system; our schools and colleges. Second is the learning that we learn from the mistakes of others and third is the learning that life teaches us through various experiences and opportunities that it throws at us. While the formal education system prepares us to become noble professionals like doctors, engineers, accountants or lawyers, it is the latter two learnings that teach an individual how to face and master his life.'

Vinay nodded in agreement.

'Also, there is one important flaw in our education system or for that matter in any education system of the world. We all read about science, history, mathematics, economics, finance in our school and college but there is no subject called real-life economics in our syllabus.'

'What is this real-life economics?' asked Vinay.

'Real-life economics or personal finance as many call it – is the subject, which deals with how you should manage your money well. Actually, it is the most important subject that any individual should learn. It is like the appetiser before you start your full meal. But in our rush to gain knowledge and make money, we forget the subject, which made Dhiru Bhai Ambani, Henry Ford and Andrew Carnegie the billionaires of their times. These self-made billionaires never saw the four walls of school but knew the concepts of real-life economics very well.'

'On the other hand there are very well-educated people – doctors, engineers, bankers and lawyers – who are experts in their domain but most of them know nothing about real-life economics, their personal finance. These people may be able to code complex algorithms, read long legal documents and complex annual reports of the companies, but they don't seem to understand everyday economics, the economics of being financially independent on a steady and ongoing basis. As a result of their ignorance, they do not teach this basic economics to their children and since this subject is never taught anywhere in school or college, people remain ignorant generation after generation. And this is the exact reason why rich get richer, the poor get poorer and the middle-class always struggle. It is because children of poor and middle-class families never get to know how to become rich.'

'Father, but people say that if you are good at studies then you will be successful and that you do not need to worry about anything else,' said Vinay looking inquisitively at his father.

Ram Prasad laughed heartily on hearing the innocent words of his son. 'You are correct but only to an extent. Do not worry if you are not able to appreciate everything. However, it is important you remember what I am telling you. When the time comes and it will come very soon as you would be earning and making money within a year, you will understand the true meaning of my words.'

Both of them had now reached the local *mithai* shop and his father ordered two hundred grams of hot and syrupy jalebi. After relishing the hot jalebis and getting a pack of another two hundred grams of jalebis for their family members, they started back home.

'Son, there is one more thing that I want you to remember. It is about the most vital thing that is necessary for one's survival, growth and prosperity.'

'And what is that?' said Vinay knowing very well that his father was definitely not talking about school and college education.

'It's about money son, about wealth and richness.'

'But, to get money you have to be greedy and make money off the sweat of the poor people. You have to be cunning and I don't think you want me to become an evil person to get lots of money.'

'Looks like you have been watching too many movies of late,' said his father.

'It's not the reality. But yes, that's how they show rich and wealthy people in the movies. Isn't it true?'

'It's completely wrong. There is a reason why they show rich and wealthy people as evil and cunning in movies. Movie producers and directors know that for every ten rich people in the society there are thousands of poor and middle-class people. And they also understand the people's psyche that if you project a certain section of people as good, that particular section of people will appreciate it and promote it because everyone wants to be projected as nice and loving people. On the other hand, if you project a certain section of people as bad, they will not like it and instead protest against it.'

'So, movie producers and directors play a game. They will show poor and middle-class people as nice and compassionate persons and rich as evil and villain. And by doing so; they earn the empathies of thousand people who are mainly from poor or middle-class against ten people who are rich. Since they produce movies to make money, they want support of thousand people even if ten people do not like it. And that is the reason why rich and wealthy people are usually shown as evil and cunning in the movies.'

Vinay was getting the taste of real-life economics for the first time. He realised how by winning the empathies of a larger section of people the movie producers are making money.

'It's one of the biggest ironies that film producers, directors and actors – who are among the richest people in the society, show rich people as evil and cunning in their movies. Have you ever watched a movie where the lead hero is from a rich family and villain from poor and middle-class? I bet there isn't a single movie where a hero from a rich family beats a villain who comes from a poor family. No producer or director in their right sense would make such a movie because if they do so, then instead of making money they would invite protests and wraths from the people. Remember, *just like there are good and bad people in rich class, there are good and bad people in middle-class and even among the poor.*'

'Now coming to the point of our discussion – the money, you should understand the true importance of money and the power and freedom that it provides in the hands of its possessor.'

'But people say money is not that important. If you are good and have a secure job then you do not need to worry about money,' said Vinay.

'*Whoever says that money is not important are usually the ones who are broke; who don't have much bank balance and who are struggling to make their ends meet,*' said his father. 'These people would say that they have a loving and supporting family and that money is not that important for them or they would say – I have the blessings of my parents, I don't need money.'

Ram Prasad thought for some time and then continued, 'Actually, these are just lame comparisons to avoid the fact that they have not been able to create and accumulate money for themselves and their family. To these people, I would simply ask – What's more important; your heart or your lungs? Maybe both, they would say.'

'Listen, money is extremely important in the areas in which it works and extremely unimportant in the areas in which it doesn't. And you need to identify and differentiate these areas. While love may make the world go round, it sure can't pay for the building of any hospitals, schools, or homes. It also can't feed anybody and neither does it pay your bills. Imagine somebody going to the bank and saying, 'Hey, I know I have to make my EMI payment for the home loan that I took from your bank.

But right now, I don't have surplus. Why don't you take love from me, I have loads of it?' What response would you think the bank manager would give to such a person? 'Security' the manager would shout and in a fraction of second, that person would be thrown out of the bank.'

Vinay started to laugh as he imagined someone offering love to a bank manager.

'Or imagine an old lady walks into a grocery store and after purchasing the fruits, vegetables and other household items, says to the cashier: 'Son, I don't have money to pay you. But I am an old lady with lot of knowledge and wisdom. Come forward and put forth your head, I will give you blessings so that you become successful.' Imagine what a scene it would create. Definitely, the cashier would go out of his mind and instead of taking blessings from her, he would say all the curse words his mouth can utter. So, here was a lady who did not understand the importance of money in the area where it works; who wanted to give blessings to someone but what did she receive; only curses.'

Vinay laughed again imagining an old lady giving blessings to the cashier at the cash counter.

'Remember, whatever may be said in praise of poverty, the fact remains that *it is not possible to live a really complete or successful life unless one is rich.* No man can rise to this greatest possible height in talent or in soul development unless he has plenty of money.'

'Our society is organised in such a way that a man must have money in order to become the possessor of these things,' continued Ram Prasad. 'If you want to become a computer engineer, you need to get a computer; if you want to become a guitar player, you need to get a guitar and services of a teacher; and if you want to become a cricketer, you need to get a good cricket kit. And for all these things, you need money to get them.'

Vinay was observing what his father was saying and was trying to grasp its essence. He was getting the first-hand experience of why money is essential to lead a complete and holistic life.

'If you want to lead a life as per your dreams then you need to have free and unrestricted use of all the things and resources, which will help you unfold your potential and fulfill your desires. *You should never be satisfied with a little if you are capable of using and enjoying more.'*

Ram Prasad looked at his son to see if he was able to convey to him the lessons of life and money that he had learnt over a period of time. Seeing that Vinay was attentive and listening to him, he continued: '*Success in life is nothing but becoming what you want to be and you can become what you want to be only by making use of things*. And to have those things you need enough money to buy them. Remember, you would not have been able to become an engineer, if I did not have sufficient money to provide you with books and fees for your coaching class.'

'I understand what you are trying to say,' said Vinay. 'But if money is so important to lead a complete and holistic life then why do people say that money is the root cause of all the evil and crime in our society?'

'It's not the money which is the root cause of crimes in our society; it is the lack of money which forces people to commit crimes. People need to have money to make their ends meet and to enjoy the luxuries of life and when they are not able to get the money to fulfil their needs and desires, they resort to crime.'
'Let me tell you something that I have learned over my life.

When does a man find his true happiness?' asked Ram Prasad.

'When he is able to achieve his dreams,' said Vinay.

'Correct. And it is every man's dream to provide happiness, goodness and benefits of the material world to his family. The man who is not able to do so has failed in his duty. It is therefore very important that everyone should try to become rich.'

'But if everyone tries to become rich then there would not be enough wealth to go around. Isn't the total wealth and money limited?' asked Vinay.

'*Wealth is not limited, rather it grows. It grows whenever man exerts energy*. It grows whenever man does some economic activity by way of growing or manufacturing something or by rendering some services.'

'How is it possible?'

'Suppose there is a plot of land. A man hires contractors, labour, carpenters and brick makers. These people then work hard and build a house for the man. The man then pays contractors, labour , carpenters and brick makers a certain amount of money for their services. Now, you may say that money paid by the man is for the value of the house that he got, so it a zero sum game for him. There is no value addition or wealth creation for him because while on the one hand he receives a house, on the other hand he has to pay equal sum of money for the house.'

'Yes,' said Vinay.

'What about the people who got paid? The contractors, the labour, the carpenters and the brick makers did not shell out anything. Yet they received money. It is because they exerted energy. They undertook the economic activity of building a house and in the process created wealth for themselves. Also once the house has been built, isn't the land on which it has been built worth more because the building is there? And isn't the land that adjoins it worth more because it is there?"

'So, always remember wealth grows in magical ways. No one can predict its limit. You just need to exert energy in a productive way and bingo, you have created wealth. You don't need to snatch money from others to become rich. People, who resort to crime to make money, do it by snatching money from others in one way or the other. They don't indulge in economic activity. They exert energy in a non-productive way because they don't create anything. And that is why our society punishes them because they try to take something without creating it.'

'I see your point. To create money and wealth, I need to exert energy in a productive manner. And yes, money is not limited; it grows whenever someone undertakes some economic activity,' said Vinay.

'Correct! Now that you are all set to start your professional life and start making money, I would like to tell you that whatever profession you choose, you should understand the importance of money and the rules that will help you in the creation and accumulation of wealth. It is only when you apply and live by these rules that you would become not only truly successful in your chosen profession but also attain peace on a personal front. *Remember, wealth will make you free of financial pressure, it will give you freedom of choice as also allow you to take advantage of various opportunities life provides you.*'

'And what are those rules for wealth creation and accumulation?'

'Hurry not, my son. For realising the true benefits of these rules, you should understand it, appreciate it and apply it with a firm commitment in your life. Hence, for your benefit I will teach you these rules step by step. I will send you letters covering the details of those rules at regular interval so that you get ample time to understand it and appreciate it. These rules will act as armours for you when you come face to face with some difficult situations. When you start to utilise these armours in the most efficient way as you may deem fit, then you will become a true winner.'

Both of them had now reached home. Vinay's mother was anxiously waiting for him as he had to pack his bags and fit in all the goodies and savouries that his mother had prepared for him.

'Don't give these sweets and *namkeen* to any of your friends there in the college. I have made these with pure ghee only for you. Eat them in the evening or whenever you feel hungry,' said his mother, packing *laddoos* for him.

After their dinner, Vinay packed all his bags before he went to sleep. There below his pillow, he found a letter by his father.

Dear Son,

While I would be sending you the Scrolls of Wealth Creation and Accumulation over a period of time, you should understand that these are not complete and exhaustive list. Remember, what I told you about the three types of learning today. It is the latter two learning – learning from the mistake of others and learning from the experiences and opportunities that life throws at you which will help you master your life. Hence, while you should learn the rules that I would tell you, you should also develop your own rules from your own experience and apply them in your life to reap their benefits.

Lovingly yours,

Ram Prasad

Vinay read the letter twice and then folded it and kept it in his pocket before falling in a deep sleep.

Three

IT BEGINS WITH
COMMITMENT

Ajay met Vinay at his residence. It was a two bedroom home in a nearby society with basic amenities. The apartment was modest though it did have all the basics furniture-wise. A bookshelf stood in the left corner of the living room and adjacent to it was the LED TV set. The sofa set placed opposite to the TV was the contemporary sofa made out of wood and fabric with soft cushions placed at its corners. The dining table near the kitchen had four chairs while the two rooms were equipped with queen-size beds and wardrobes. Vinay later told Ajay that he had purchased the furniture from Allahabad, which he had transported to Bengaluru.

Vinay was living with his wife. They had one son and a daughter. While Vinay was working in a chip making company based out of USA, his wife Ananya was working in a start-up company providing cloud services to various big firms.

After tea and snacks with Vinay and his family, Ajay told Vinay about his predicament. He told him about his layoff – how he had fallen into this unpleasant situation. Now he found it difficult to pay his EMI and his credit card payments. He also told him about Priya's sabbatical leave, to take care of Kiara. However, though he was confident of getting another a job within two months but he feared that in case that doesn't happen then his source of income would come down to zero.

Vinay was very much aware of the precarious lifestyle that Ajay was leading. Many times he had thought of informing Ajay that he was living a life, which is not sustainable and that it would crumble very soon if he doesn't change his habits and attitude towards money. However fearing that Ajay might get offended, he never broached this topic. Now he was feeling guilty that he had let his friend fall into the debt trap.

'I can help you by lending you money in case you are not able to find the job but that will not solve your problem in the long run,' said Vinay after thinking for some time.

'You are getting it wrong my friend,' said Ajay. 'I have not come here for seeking monetary help from you as I am sure I will get a job in next two months. What I have come to you for is to understand and gain knowledge and wisdom that you seem to possess and which you have utilised for creating wealth and assets for yourself and your family. I want to get out of the debt trap that I have fallen into and just like you, I too want to become stable and wealthy.'

'Why do you say that?' Vinay was testing Ajay whether

he was serious about changing his lifestyle, his habits and his views towards money.

'Because in the past one week I have realised that even though I have been working hard and earning well, I am not able to support my family now. I have bought a home, a car and many more goods for which I am now finding it difficult to make the payments. I feel broke. Yet when I see you, I observe that you have done pretty well for yourself. In addition to owning a home for your living, you also have another home which brings rental income to you. I wish I too had a similar apartment whose rental income would have taken care of my expenses in my present gloomy period. I wish I was also rich. I wish I also had lots of money,' said Ajay feeling depressed.

'You don't need to be sad,' Vinay tried to console him by tapping his right hand on Ajay's shoulder. 'All you need is to understand that merely having money will not solve your problem. If you think lack of money is your problem and getting more money will solve all your problems; then you are completely mistaken. *Most people, given more money, only get into more debt.* Take your case. When you had started working, you started with a smaller salary. At that time, you were free. You earned, you went to restaurants, movies and you enjoyed. Soon you were promoted, your salary increased and you were happy to see your revised and upgraded CTC. But your happiness didn't last. You purchased car, you bought home, furniture etc. and before you could realise; you were deep down in debt.'

'But I feel that if I had more money, then all my problems would be solved and I would be happy. It is because of lack of money that I am not able to pay my EMIs for my home and car,' said Ajay who was still looking dejected.

'I guess you would have heard of Jim Rohn,' said Vinay.

'No, I've never heard of him,' replied Vinay.

'Jim Rohn was an American entrepreneur, author and motivational speaker. He was guided by Earl Shoaff, another entrepreneur, in his formative years. So one day, Jim had asked the same question to Shoaff. Jim said that if he had more money then he'd be happy. To this, Mr Shoaff had replied – *"The key to happiness is not more money. Happiness is an art to be studied and practiced. More money will only make you more of what you already are."* '

'I didn't get it, how more money will make me more of what I already am?' asked Ajay.

'What Mr Shoaff meant was that merely having more money will not change you from what you really are. More money will only send you more quickly to your destination. So, if you are inclined to be unhappy you'll remain unhappy with more money, though you would be crying on a silver mattress rather than on cotton coir but you would still be crying. If you are inclined to drink a little, more money will enable you to waste yourself in liquor. If you are inclined to creating terror and killing, then more money will provide you with opportunities to create more terror and kill masses on a larger scale. And if you are inclined to waste money and take debt and loan, then with more money you will only waste more and get into bigger debt.'

'On the other hand if you are generous, more money will simply allow you to be more generous. If you are a person who likes to help people, then with more money you will be able to help a larger number of people. If you are inclined to teach people, then with more money you will teach a lot more people.'

'Remember, *money is nothing but an amplifier. It amplifies your internal habit.* So, if you want to be rich and happy then you need to change your perspective and habit about money. Listen, when I say: if money is your problem, then money cannot be the solution.'

'Then what is the solution?'

'Literacy; Financial Literacy is the solution. You need to be financially intelligent to come out of the mess that you have presently put yourself in.'

'Sorry, I didn't get what you are trying to say,' Ajay looked a little surprised as he was hearing the word "Financial Literacy" for the first time.

'Intelligence solves problems and produces money. Money without financial intelligence is money soon gone.[1] Most people fail to realise that in life, it's not how much money you make but how much money you keep that matters. My father always used to say: *earning money is an art and keeping your earned money with yourselves is a different art.* Most of the people learn the first art by going to school and college but they never learn the second art and that is the reason they struggle throughout their life.'

'They think that if they can earn more money, then they will be better off. So they start working hard. They would work day and night; would miss their kids' school program, would not attend social functions at their home town since they don't have time for that as they are busy in their work life. Very soon, their hard work is recognised and appreciated They get their desired promotion and increment. Yet what happens after the increment? Nothing! Their struggle continues. Why is it so? It is

---

[1]Financial Intelligence and Financial Literacy has been greatly advocated by Robert Kiyosaki in his book *Rich Dad Poor Dad.*

because they haven't realised that it is not how much they make but how much they keep with themselves that really matters. So, if you want to solve your problem you need to learn the second art. The art of keeping your money with yourself to allow it grow with time. This comes only with financial literacy.'

'But how do we learn about financial literacy? I guess no school, college or university teaches its students the art of keeping the money with oneself to then let it grow with time.'

'For that you need to observe the rules, which govern the flow and growth of money. All of us have studied Newton's Laws of Motion, which govern the motion of an object in response to some external force applied on it. We observe these laws in our day to day life and thank Sir Isaac for having taught us these rules. These rules laid the foundation of classical mechanics and helped in the invention of many machines and tools which made our lives much easier.'

'*And just like an object is governed by the Newton's Laws of Motion; flow of money and its growth is governed by some other set of rules too.* However, these set of rules have been kept in secret by the Rich and passed on only to their children. That is the reason, we have generations of family who are rich because they know these rules and play the game in accordance with the rules. However unlike Sir Isaac Newton, nobody has published these rules and never taught them in schools and colleges and hence most of the people; the poor and the middle-class are not aware of these rules.'

'Yet there are few people who are not born into rich family but are keen observers. They learn these rules; the laws which govern the flow and growth of money by themselves and/or by looking for them from someone who already know these rules and then play the game as per the rules. My father was one such person. He learned these rules from one of the richest man in Allahabad and then passed on to me and I too learned some of them on my own. My father calls these rules; these laws which govern the flow and growth of money as 'Scroll of Wealth Creation and Accumulation.' I have been very diligent in following these rules and as you see, these rules have helped me a lot in wealth creation and its accumulation.'

'So you mean to say that for becoming rich, you just have to simply follow certain rules.'

'Yes, you need to follow the rules of wealth creation and accumulation. But let me tell you that following these rules is not an easy task. It needs the character and determination of a person with strong will. It needs discipline. And yes, these rules will not make you rich overnight. It will take time. Yet I assure you that you will learn how to become rich – steadily and surely – over the course of your working life. It's the tortoise's approach to wealth and not the hare's.'

'I guess, I will give it a try,' said Ajay half-heartedly. He was dissatisfied because he was expecting more than just following simple rules to create wealth To ensure a better quality of life. He had expected that Vinay would teach him certain tricks or would give him some tips to become rich. However, here he was being asked to follow certain simple rules.

'I think you are still not ready to learn the lessons of Wealth Creation and Accumulation. I am sorry, but I cannot help you in your journey.'

'I didn't mean that,' Ajay was trying to defend himself. 'I think I am ready to learn the lessons and I will do and practice whatever is required to become rich.'

'Are you sure, you want to be rich?' Vinay was again testing Ajay's commitment.

'Of course, I want to be rich.'

Vinay was smiling on hearing Ajay's response. He then spoke, 'You sound like almost everyone. If you ask anyone that if they want to be rich; what would you expect them to answer? Everyone would answer the same as you answered; that is, they would say they want to be rich. Yet not everybody is rich. Why is it so?'

'It is because they do not put in effort to be rich,' replied Ajay.

'That is one of the reasons but the actual reason is something different. Everybody wants to have money even then they don't have it. Actually, there is difference between *wanting* and *having*. *Wanting* doesn't necessarily lead to *having*.' Vinay paused for some time, then continued, 'Let me tell you something about "want" Harv Eker, the famous personal finance coach says that actually there are three levels of so-called want. The first level as you are saying is "I *want* to be rich." It's another way of saying "I'll take the money if someone gives it to me."

'Have you ever noticed a two-year-old kid who is hungry?' continued Vinay. 'When he is hungry he definitely wants milk to satisfy his hunger but what does he do to get the milk? Nothing! He simply sits there and starts to cry. Only when his parents hear him cry then they feed him. Most of the poor and middle-class people are like that two-year-old kid, in the sense that they want money but will not take any actions to gather or keep a hold of money. They will simply sit and complain. In the real world nobody will come and give them money just because they cry. "Want" alone is useless. Wealth does not come from mere "want." How do we know this is true? Just take a real world check – millions and billions of people want to be rich; relatively few are.'

'Then what is the second level of want?' asked Ajay as he was getting curious about whatever Vinay was telling him.

'The second level of want is 'I *choose* to be rich.' This entails decision to be rich. It is similar to a teenage boy who stands up, goes to refrigerator and takes out milk to satisfy his hunger. Here, he does not simply sit down to cry to get the milk. He takes action. Now what happens when the refrigerator is empty? He will inform his parents that there is no milk in the house and chances are that his parents would give him money to buy a packet of milk from a nearby grocery store. Most of the upper-middle-class people behave like this because they are dependent on their employer, government etc. to be rich. Choosing is a much stronger energy and goes hand-in-hand with being responsible for creating your reality. *Choosing* is better than *wanting* but it is not the best.'

'Ok! What is the best?' asked Ajay.

'Best comes at the third level of want. It is a decision. "I *commit* to being rich." Committment requires unreservedly to devote with dedication to achieve a goal. This means – hold absolutely nothing back; give the whole 100% of everything you've got to achieve wealth. It means to be ready to do whatever it takes for as long as it takes. This is the warrior's way. For a warrior or a soldier, failure is not an option. The warrior's way is simple: '*I will be rich or I will die on the way but I will never stop.*' This is the way rich people become *rich*. It is similar to an adult who needs to get milk. Seeing that there is no milk in the house, what does he do? He does not ask his parents.

Rather he goes out, works hard, earns money and then buy's the milk for himself and his family. He takes responsibility for himself. He takes actions necessary to get the milk. In this case he is not dependent on anyone. *He is free.*'

'So if I want to become rich, I need to commit myself to being rich,' said Ajay.

'Yes! *Poor people want to become rich and hence they are never able to become rich. Middle-class choose to be rich. But Rich People are committed to being rich and that is why they are rich.* Vince Lombardi, the famous American football player, coach and executive said once '*Most people fail not because of lack of desire, but because of lack of commitment.*' Becoming rich is not an easy task. Getting rich takes focus, courage, knowledge, expertise, 100% of your effort, a never give-up attitude and a deep desire and commitment. You also have to believe deep down in your heart that you can create wealth and you absolutely deserve it.

'Let me tell you something about W H Murray. Mr Murray was a Scottish mountaineer and writer. He had written a passage during one of his first Himalayan expeditions which beautifully captures the effect and essence of being committed to a cause. I have a copy of that passage. Read it and then you will realise the importance of commitment.'

Vinay then got up, searched for a piece of page in his small library and gave it to Ajay to read.

Until one is committed, there is hesitancy, the chance to draw back. Concerning all acts of initiative (and creation), there is one elementary truth, the ignorance of which kills countless ideas and splendid plans: that the moment one definitely commits oneself, then Providence moves too. All sorts of things occur to help one that would never otherwise have occurred. A whole stream of events issues from the decision, raising in one's favour all manner of unforeseen incidents and meetings and material assistance, which no man could have dreamed would have come his way. I learned a deep respect for one of Goethe's couplets: Whatever you can do, or dream you can do, begin it. Boldness has genius, power and magic in it. Begin it now.[2]

As Ajay read the passage, he realised the importance of commitment. He gave the paper back to Vinay who then put it back in place. Vinay then got back to Ajay and said, 'What does this passage say? It simply says that Universe will assist you, guide you, support you and even create miracles for you. First, make a commitment to take action.'

'I see your point,' Ajay was thoughtful in his words. 'To bring richness to my life, first I need to commit myself to create wealth that is without the thought of failure I need to execute plans to attain my goal. And to execute the plans, I need to learn the rules of flow and growth of money; the rules of wealth creation and accumulation.'

'You have always been a good learner, my friend,' exclaimed Vinay. 'But before I share these rules with you let me tell you something much more important.'

Ajay nodded in positive affirmation to let Vinay know that he is listening to him and is desirous to learn from him.

'Each and every one of us has a particular mindset with regard to money and success built in one of the corners of our

---

[2]http://blog.gaiam.com/quotes/authors/wh-murray

brain. Let's call it Money Mind. *Money Mind* is nothing but the notion and feelings that we attach to money and anything related to money. *It is our way of being in relationship with our money.* This mindset gets developed over a period since our birth and is highly influenced by our childhood conditioning about the money. And the amount of wealth that we accumulate depends a lot on this mindset. It is like a design, a blueprint that has been programmed in our mind with regard to money. And just as the blueprint is, so will be the final outcome – that is our capacity to earn and hold money depends a lot on our *Money Mind.*'

Vinay paused for some time, looked at Ajay and then continued, 'Imagine a jar of one litre capacity. If you fill water in it, then the maximum amount of water that it can hold is one litre. It can't hold anything more than a litre. Our Money Mind is very similar to the jar and the water of the jar is nothing but the money. To become rich, you just cannot increase the flow of water into the jar because it will not hold more than its capacity no matter what is the flow of the water. You need to make your jar bigger. And once your jar is big, the water will automatically fill it.'

'So, how do we make our jar big?' asked Ajay.

'You can do that by changing your thought process; by improving your Money Mind – by having a Rich Mindset.'

'Sorry, but I didn't get you.'

'Let me tell you some hard-hitting facts,' said Vinay. 'Suppose there are two people who are equally eager to learn the rules of wealth creation and accumulation. They are equally committed to the cause and are ready to take all the necessary actions. And I tell and explain to them the rules in an unbiased way. But one person has a rich mindset – his Money Mind is set at a higher level or to say he has a bigger jar and the other person has a poor mindset – his Money Mind is set at a lower level than the other person; he has a smaller jar. Can you guess how much wealth the two will accumulate after learning the rules and applying them in their life? Will the two earn and make the same amount of money? Certainly not!'

'I see your point. I need to change my thought process. I need to change the way I think about money. I need to increase my capacity to hold the money and then only I can become rich,' said Ajay.

'Correct,' said Vinay. 'The person who has a rich mindset will earn and accumulate much more wealth than the person with a poor mindset. *Most Rich people think in very similar ways.* It's not an exact science, but for the most part, rich people think in a certain way and poor people think in a completely different way and those ways of thinking determine their actions and therefore determine their results.'

'In the process of becoming rich and accumulating wealth, rich people focus a lot on their thought process and on their personality development. They learn various skills. They improve their Money Mind –that is they increase the capacity of their jar by thinking and approaching a problem like a rich person would do. They understand the simple rule that *to have more than what you've got today; you have to become more than what you are today.*'

'Also, rich people by improving their Money Mind understand the responsibilities that come with increased income. They increase their capacity to create and hold a larger amount of money. So, if someone hands over a cheque of one crore rupees to you, then you better hurry up and have a rich mindset, otherwise in no time you will be back to square one. A very rich man had once said: '*If you took all the money in the world and divide it equally among everybody, it would soon be back in the same pockets it was before.*' It's hard to keep something, which has not been obtained through improvement in your Money Mind and Wealth Jar.'

'Remember, your income will rarely exceed your Money Mind; your Wealth Jar. Whatever you call: Rich Mindset, Money Mind or Wealth Jar; all are the same thing. Sometimes, your income may take a lucky jump, but unless you learn how to handle the responsibilities that come with it, it will usually shrink back to the amount you can handle. It all boils down to this – if your subconscious Money Mind; your wealth jar is not set for richness and success; nothing you learn, nothing you know and nothing you do will make much of a difference. And that is why I want you to first have a *Rich Mindset* before you begin your journey of richness and wealth accumulation. Because, if you want to become rich, all you have to do is copy how rich people think.'

'I see your point,' said Ajay in agreement. 'But how do I get the Rich Mindset? Where do I learn how rich people think and act? How do I increase the capacity of my Wealth Jar?'

'For that you need to get yourself baptised,' Vinay paused for some time and then said 'Financially Baptised.'

'Sorry?'

'Do you remember Manisha; our batchmate from NIT?' asked Vinay.

'Yes, the one who has now turned into a successful entrepreneur?'

'Yes. Before becoming successful, she has failed several times. I want you to go meet her. Learn from her what it takes to have a rich mindset so that when we meet again then you are ready to learn the rules of wealth creation and accumulation,' Vinay said – with a smile.

Four

THINK RICH TO BECOME RICH

anisha was a batchmate of Ajay and Vinay from NIT Allahabad. After completing graduation, she had gone on to pursue her MBA from IIM Kozhikode. It was during her internship at one of the leading fashion retail stores of the country that she got an idea for starting her own venture. She contacted few of her close friends and discussed the idea with them. But only two of them promised to work alongside her after completion of their studies.

Manisha and her two friends started the venture with full zeal with the borrowed money from their family members. As their sales number grew, they thought of scaling up the business and approached the bank for loans. Since they didn't have a fully set up company and because they had not got their venture registered; they were unable to get a corporate loan and had to borrow money from the Bank as Personal Loan at a very high interest rate. As they scaled up their business, opened another centre and hired some support staff, their sales somehow nosedived. The resultant cash crunch along with high rental payments for their office, interest payment for the bank loan and salaries to be paid to the support staff led to things going haywire. Soon there was a dispute among the three partners about sustainability of the business and her two friends left the partnership to join some MNC. Manisha was heartbroken since within a year her dream was shattered as she was unable to carry the business on her shoulders alone. When her business was shut down – she had to face the first major failure of her life.

Her parents then started coaxing her to join some company but she had a different mindset. She wanted to do something of her own. After researching the market as also considering her interests and talents, she came up with another plan. She started a catering business. She focused on providing cut fruits, sprouts and other healthy meal packs as evening snacks to office employees. She hired two technical staff to create a website for her business where the menu would be displayed – her customers could place orders. She then hired a few delivery boys. After making this skeletal infrastructure Mansiha contacted a few corporate clients to get repeat business. Yet again, before her business could gain a foothold, another venture started by a group of college graduates on the same business model captured the market. Rather soon she had to close her venture. Her next failure came within a period of six months.

Now she had started questioning her potential and belief in herself. It was at this point of time that she met Vinay. She told him about her recent failures in the businesses. After enquiring about the businesses – what went wrong in each venture, Vinay asked her about her family background, the source of income for her family and the spending and investment style that her family followed. It didn't take much time for Vinay to realise that Manisha's mindset was not set for success that she has been trying to achieve. He understood that Manisha had everything required to achieve success: she had a burning desire to set up a venture on her own, she was truly committed towards her goal as well as a thorough understanding of the start-up ecosystem. Yet she was failing. It was mainly because of the faulty *Money Mind* that has been programmed in her subconsciousness, which was not letting her achieve her goal. She still had the Poor Mindset, which was the reason for her failures.

Vinay then told Manisha that she needs to change her mindset if she wants to achieve her goal. He told her that almost all the rich and successful people think in the same way and she needs to learn the same. He told her about various ways in which Rich people think differently from poor and middle-class people. He explained to her that given a problem; be it in business, job or life; rich and successful people would approach it in an altogether different way than the approach taken by a normal poor or middle-class people.

Eventually, Manisha realised this failing as also became aware of how her own thoughts held her back from success and wealth. She then started using what she had learned from Vinay. She started to copy rich people both in terms of their business strategies and thinking strategies. In her next venture, which she started with her husband, the first thing she did was to commit herself to success and then she started to play to win. She swore that she would focus and not even consider the possibility of the failure of this business until she was a millionaire.

She also began to challenge her own mental approach whenever she thought of financially negative or counterproductive ways. She researched the market more comprehensively as well as started to take calculated risks. She began looking for opportunities rather than just a focus on obstacles. With every small failure she didn't back out. She learnt the lessons and moved ahead. Throughout her journey, her husband stood as a strong pillar to guide her as well as create a backup in case something does not go as per the plan. Very soon, she had set up a successful online lingerie e-commerce site.

Ajay met Manisha in her new office. It was a small premises in one of the eastern suburbs of Bengaluru and housed around thirty odd employees. Many of the employees didn't have a dedicated cubicle for themselves, even shared desks among them. Manisha welcomed him in her cabin as she enquired about his personal and professional life. She congratulated him on becoming a father. Hearing about his soon to be joblessness did feel sorry for him. Ajay then informed her about his visit to Vinay. He told her that it was Vinay who had suggested he go to meet her to get *Financially Baptised*.

Manisha smiled as she heard about Vinay. She understood the task that Vinay has assigned her as an aid for Ajay to get financially baptised; to set his *Money Mind* for success and to help him have a *Rich Mindset*. She remembered her promise to Vinay and thanked her fortunes that gave her this opportunity so quickly.

'I guess Vinay would have told you about *Money Mind* and *Wealth Jar*,' said Manisha.

'Yes. He told that all of us have a *Money Mind* built in one of the corners of our brain. It's our relationship with the money. But I was not able to appreciate it completely. I went home and thought over it. I realised that having a *Wealth Jar* with a bigger capacity will help me in holding the money but how does this *Money Mind* help to create money?' asked Ajay.

'You would have probably heard of lottery winners; people who by chance and luck make a huge amount of money. Yet, what happens to those monies? Research has shown again and again that regardless of the size of their winnings, most lottery winners return to their original financial state, the amount they can comfortably handle. Why? It is because they have a smaller *Wealth Jar* so that they cannot handle a bigger amount of money. So, this answers why having a bigger *Wealth Jar* is necessary to hold money; which I guess you are already able to appreciate.'

'Yes,' replied Ajay.

'Now, let's come to your question about how *Money Mind* helps in creating money. Have you noticed that when self-made millionaires lose their money, they usually have it back within a relatively short time? They create it back for themselves,' asked Manisha.

'I have read about few billionaires in the West who lost all their money but recovered quickly to get it back. In India, I am not able to recall any such cases,' said Ajay.

'Well at home, Amitabh Bachchan is a good example. Big B as we call him is a legend – he has been called the Superstar of the Millennium. Very few people know about his bankruptcy. In the year 1999, he had almost lost everything that he had yet a couple of years later got it all back again and much more.'

'I didn't know about such a story.' Ajay was curious to know how his favourite superstar had lost his wealth only to then earn everything back.

Manisha then explained to Ajay that how Big B had started the company called Amitabh Bachchan Corporation Ltd (ABCL) which specialised in film production and event management and how the 46th edition of the Miss World beauty pageant in Bengaluru put a strain on ABCL's Balance Sheet by bringing in a loss of over ₹4 crores. She told him that in the year 1999, after a series of flop movies Big B was in such a financial mess that he had to rush to the regulatory authority to seek protection under the bankruptcy laws.

'So, at the age of 57 when a normal person starts planning for his retirement, Big B was in a big financial crisis as he had almost lost all he had earned. The situation was more serious as he didn't have any movie lined up in his kitty,' said Manisha.

'So, how did he get back everything?' asked Ajay.

'Big B had lost his money but not his *Money Mind*. He still had his *Rich Mindset* intact. With such a mindset anybody would bounce back just as he did. He didn't accept the defeat but looked for work. He contacted Yash Chopra and got to work in the movie Mohabattein. Luckily, then *Kaun Banega Crorepati* (KBC) happened, which changed his fortunes. Imagine starting your life from zero at the age of retirement. It would seem almost impossible for a normal person but for people with a Rich Mindset it's not that difficult.'

'It's truly an inspirational story' said Ajay.

'Indeed it's an inspirational story,' said Manisha. 'Well, do you know about Jim Rohn?'

'Yes, Vinay told me last week about him that he was a great entrepreneur, author and motivational speaker,' replied Ajay.

'After meeting with Vinay, I too read what Mr Rohn says about wealth, success and happiness. it has greatly helped me. I would recommend his works to you. Anyway, coming to *Money Mind* and *Rich Mindset* that we were discussing, Jim Rohn has described about our *Money Mind* – about our mindset – very beautifully. He says – *"Give a million dollars to someone who does not possess the attitude, the mindset of a rich person and that person will most likely lose it. But take away all the wealth from a truly rich person and in no time he or she will build a new fortune. Why? It is because those who earn their millionaire status develop the skills, knowledge and experience to duplicate the process again and again."*

'Remember, *the greatest value in becoming a truly rich and wealthy person is in the skills, knowledge, discipline and leadership qualities you'll develop and imbibe in reaching that elevated status.* It's the experience you'll acquire in planning and developing strategies. It's the inner strength you'll develop to have enough courage, commitment and willpower to attract money. And once you have done it, then to increase your wealth all you need to do is to repeat the process.'

Manisha paused for some time and then continued, 'Now that you have come to get financially baptised, I will help you to have a *Rich Mindset* as well as help you set your *Money Mind* for success and richness. I will explain to you about three different ways in which Rich people think differently from the poor and middle-class people and then you can choose to think in ways that will support you in your happiness, success and wealth creation and accumulation instead of ways they don't.'

As she looked at her watch, Manisha saw it was almost lunch time. Her husband had gone to meet certain suppliers to negotiate a contract that they were trying to finalise for the past few weeks. Manisha then invited Ajay for the lunch to a nearby restaurant to which he readily agreed. During lunch both of them discussed about their good old college days up to how their friends were doing in their present lives. Ajay also noticed how Manisha has changed from a shy girl in engineering college to a confident girl who plays the game on her own terms. After all she is now the CEO of a company.

After returning to Manisha's office, Ajay was all ready to learn from her about how to have the *Rich Mindset* – how to set his *Money Mind* for wealth and success.

Difference #1
Rich People believe 'I create my own destiny.'
Poor People believe 'I can't change much. It's already written.'

'You would have heard people telling that their fate is written and that is why they are not able to achieve success. They would tell that probably it's the result of some past sin that they are struggling so much in their present life,' said Manisha looking at Ajay.

'Yes, I have heard people telling something similar,' said Ajay.

'Do you remember any of those people who say that their destiny or fate is already written – it just so happens they are successful?'

'No,' said Vinay after thinking for some time.

'When people say that their destiny is already written, they simply excuse themselves from taking any actions. They relieve themselves of the responsibility and starts blaming their fate for their failures. In order to acquit themselves of the guilt of having failed, they try to convince themselves that it's not them but their fate which is responsible for their failures. And that is the reason they struggle throughout their life, because they do not take any action to improve their life.'

'If you want to create and accumulate wealth, if you want to be successful then it is very important for you to believe that you are at the driver's seat of your life, especially your financial life,' continued Manisha. 'If you don't believe this, then you indirectly believe that you have little or no control over your life and therefore you have little or no control over your financial success. And with such an attitude you will never be able to take actions necessary to bring success and richness in your life.'

'You need to understand that *you are the one who creates your success; that you are the one who creates your mediocrity and that you are the one creating your struggle around money and success.* Once you realise this, you will find ways which will lead you to your goal. Remember, *accepting full responsibility is one of the highest form of human maturity – and one of the hardest. It's the day you pass from childhood to adulthood.*'

'If taking responsibility for one's life is so helpful then why everyone doesn't take responsibility and start creating their own life?' asked Ajay.

'That is because it is easy to play the role of victim and blame others for their present state than to take responsibility for themselves. If you play the role of victim and blame others then you do not need to take any action to improve your present state. Also, when you blame outside forces instead of looking within, you don't need to face your own weakness and failings. You put the responsibility on others – you pass on the baton to your employer, to your manager and/or subordinates, to the Government, to the economy, to the stock market and most importantly to your parents and your family members. You want them to take action on your behalf to improve your present situation. However, if you take responsibility for your present state and your life then you need to take action to improve it. And most people prefer to talk rather than take actions.'

'Also most people want everyone else but themselves to change; and that is one of the reasons that they blame. By blaming others, people deprive themselves of the opportunity to change and improve. They don't know that *it is much easier to change themselves than everyone else.*'

'If you keep shifting responsibilities to something or the other, you'll always be broke and disillusioned. You'll never earn enough. But when you start thinking in terms of 'me' instead of 'them,' you'll experience a surge in personal growth and income.'

Manisha looked at Ajay who was looking attentively at her and then she continued, 'Another way in which people constantly put themselves in the path to failure is by justifying and giving excuses.'

'How justifying stops someone from achieving success?' asked Ajay.

'Justifying and giving excuses is nothing but an indirect way of blaming others,' said Manisha. 'When you give excuse, you are actually trying to protect yourself and pass on the blame to others. The poor and middle-class people will try to justify their present situation by stating 'Money is not that important to me.' And they would be the same person who would wake up early and rush to the office. These same people would stay late in the office just to project themselves as a hardworking employee expecting their boss to notice their late stay so that they can get better appraisal and better hike. But when it comes to their low bank balance they would say, I work not for money but because I love working. Nothing can be farther from the truth.'

'When you are justifying and giving excuses, you are again passing on the responsibility to someone else. *Remember, either you create million excuses or you create million rupees. But you cannot create both.'*

Ajay realised how he was blaming his organisation when he was being laid off. He had blamed the economy for shrinking of the job market. He had even started blaming his fate that despite being such a star performer – he was being asked to leave. However, wisdom prevailed over him; all thanks to his wife Priya, he started looking for solutions to improve his financial health. Now he was thanking both Vinay and Manisha who helped him at the right time when he needed them.

'Apart from blaming, giving excuses and playing the role of victim, poor and middle-class people also enjoy complaining,' said Manisha.

'But how does complaining stop someone from creating wealth and becoming rich?' asked Ajay.

'There is this universal law of attraction. It states that 'like attracts like.'[3] In other words; whatever you focus on, you attract into your life and it expands. When you are complaining, you focus on what's wrong with your life. Whatever you focus on expands, the wrongs in your life will increase and you will get more and more opportunities to complain.'

---

[3]Law of attraction given to the maxim 'like attracts like' is a New Thought philosophy used to sum up the idea that by focussing on positive or negative thoughts a person brings positive or negative experiences into his/her life. This law has been made popular by Rhonda Byrne in her book *The Secret.*

'Have you ever noticed that complainers usually have a tough life?' asked Manisha. 'It seems that everything that could go wrong does go wrong for them. And they will always be complaining. In many instances, there may not be any problem in reality but since they are in the habit of complaining, they complain and lose out the opportunity to appreciate and be grateful for all the goodness in their life. But when you are not complaining you are not focusing on wrong things in your life and it will not expand further. Also when you are not complaining you start taking responsibility for yourself and then you look for possible solutions which results in action and thereby yield results.'

'Then why do people complain?' asked Ajay.

'Complaining, just like blaming – is like a capsule, which helps people reduce stress. They alleviate the stress of failure. You would notice that after complaining about anything, you feel relieved though it would last only for few moments. When you are blaming, giving excuses or complaining, you project yourself as a victim of your circumstances and apart from getting some attention and sympathy from others it doesn't help you in anyway. Nobody would move a single stone on your blaming and complaining. You stand there at the same place where you were standing before blaming and complaining. However, if you take responsibility, you elevate yourself to a higher level and start looking down at the problem to find the possible solutions.'

'It's time to decide,' said Manisha. 'You can be a victim *or* you can be rich and successful, but you can't be both. *Every time you blame, give excuse or complain you are missing the opportunity to improve your life*. You must realise that it is you and only you who create your life and wealth. And hence choice to bring wealth and success in your life is entirely dependent on you and no one else.'

Ajay understood the difference in approach taken between the rich and successful people with the one taken by normal people. He realised that very often he used to blame and complain about everything wrong in his life. Now he decided that he wouldn't be the victim anymore, rather he would take responsibility for his life and would create his own destiny. He would take all the necessary actions to improve his life including his financial well-being because he had understood that it is the action that counts and not the words. He promised himself that this day he would cross over from childhood to adulthood.

Difference #2
Rich People focus on Opportunities.
Poor People focus on Obstacles.

'Now let us discuss another point where the thinking process of Rich people and Poor people differ,' said Manisha. 'Do you remember the famous archery test that Guru Dronacharya had conducted for his students?'

'Are you talking about the tale from Mahabharata where Guru Dronacharya asks Kauravas and Pandavas to hit the eye of a wooden bird that he had put on a branch of a tree?' said Ajay.

'Yes' said Manisha. 'In the test Dronacharya asks his students to hit the eye of the bird from a distance of hundred yards. But before the students were to release the arrow, he used to ask each of his students "What do you see?" and then each students would reply something like "I see the bird, the leaves and the branches" or "I see the bird, the tree, you and my brothers and cousins." On hearing such responses he did not allow them to release the arrow. However when Arjuna came and took the aim, his reply was "I see the bird's head and its eyes." When Dronacharya probed further whether he was able to see anything like legs and wings of the bird, then Arjuna's reply was "I see nothing but the bird's eye." Then Dronacharya ordered "Fire!" and no sooner were the words uttered, that the wooden bird fell on the ground with an arrow in its eye.'

'I know the story, but what is its importance in wealth creation and accumulation?' asked Ajay.

'Do you know why Dronacharya did not allow his other students to take the shot?'

'It's because other students were not able to take the proper aim.'

'Correct; the other students were giving too much attention on obstacles like leaves, branches, trees it meant if they were allowed to take the shot they would have missed the target. Only Arjuna was able to focus entirely on his aim, his goal; the bird's eye and that is why he was bang on his target. He released his arrow with the target in his mind and nothing else.'

'But how does it help in wealth creation?'

'Don't be impatient,' said Manisha lightly admonishing Ajay. 'In our life, achieving success and creating wealth is like the bird's eyes and the difficulties that we face in our journey of achieving success are nothing but the leaves and branches of the tree. If we focus too much on obstacles then we will fail. But if we focus only on our goal then nothing can stop us from achieving success. The path from the bow to the bird's eye was same for every student. It was filled with both obstacles and opportunities. However, all the students like most of the people, focused on obstacles and were not able to hit the target. But, Arjuna showed the characteristics of a true warrior, the characteristics of Rich and Successful people and focussed only on his goal and hence was able to hit the target.'

'Rich people see opportunities, Poor people see obstacles,' continued Manisha. 'Rich people see potential growth, Poor people see potential loss. Rich people focus on rewards, Poor people focus on risks. And if you are seeing only obstacles, potential losses and risks, then you will never take actions to realise your goal. You will convince yourself by saying that it's too difficult and impractical. Better I stay where I am. Yet rich people prefer to see the other side of the coin. They see opportunities, potential growth and rewards. They know that to succeed financially, they need to take actions; to do something, to invest in something or to start something.'

'I see your point,' said Ajay while he was deep in his thoughts.

'Let me give you an example from my life,' said Manisha. Ajay looked at her with full attention.

'When I started my second venture; the food catering business I did my entire homework. I had carried out the market research, identified the needs of the market which I could have filled and set up my unit with few support staff. I even had established contacts with the corporate clients and had brought in the best cook available. However, even before my business could run at its full pace, a competitor captured the market.'

'At that time I became nervous because my competitor was going full gaga with its promotional campaign, doling out offers and discounts. I did not have much funds and I was not able to match them both in terms of promoting my business and in pricing. I started looking at the obstacles. I started focusing on their strengths and my weakness and started justifying myself why I might not be able to compete with them. I did not realise that though my competitor is doing well, there is space left for other players to flourish. I did not focus on the opportunity. Rather I kept on staring at the obstacles. And what happened? I had to close down my business. Now I realise had I continued my business with a focus on my product offering, along with the opportunity that was available to me – I would have succeeded in that business.'

'In retrospect it is easy to analyse our mistakes but how we make our choice at that moment decides our fate,' said Ajay.

'Yes, you speak truth. The decision that we make at a particular moment comes from our mindset. And that is why setting our *Money Mind* for success is so important. Had I set my *Money Mind* for wealth and success then I would have looked at opportunity intensely and would not have concentrated at the obstacles. And then probably I would have succeeded in the catering business.'

'Do you know why rich and successful people are able to see opportunities so easily whereas Poor people find it difficult to look for opportunities?' asked Manisha.

'No idea.'

'It is because Rich people expect themselves to succeed. They have confidence in their abilities and strengths, they have confidence in their creativity and they believe that if anything goes wrong then they can find another way to succeed. Poor people on the other hand, expect to fail. They lack confidence in themselves and their abilities. They believe that should things not work out, it would be catastrophic and that the whole sky would fall down. And because they constantly see obstacles, they are usually unwilling to take a risk and with no risk there is usually no reward.'

'If you want to be successful, then you should have faith in your abilities like rich people have in themselves. Remember people can rise to unbelievable heights when situation becomes desperate: A woman can lift a two-ton car to save her child; a man can survive starvation and disease in a concentration camp because he dreams of seeing his family and prisoners of war do beat all the tortures inflicted upon them by the enemies only because they hope to return to their motherland. So accept the fact that everybody is remarkable including you. Thrive on your uniqueness! Reach down inside yourself and bring out more of your remarkable human gifts. They are there, waiting to be discovered and used. You just need to dig a deep and believe in yourself.'

Ajay was silent trying to grasp whatever Manisha was saying. He realised the mantra to success is nothing but believing in your abilities, focussing on the opportunities and then taking the necessary action to achieve the goal.

'Let me give you another example of how our perspective can change the results for us. There is this Biblical story of the battle between David and Goliath. Goliath was a giant Philistine warrior who was over nine feet tall. The whole of Israel army was terrified of Goliath including Saul, the King of Israel. One day David, who was a teenager and the youngest son of Jesse, was sent to the battle lines by his father to bring back the news of his brothers. When David reached the battlefield he saw his brothers and the entire Israel army in fear of Goliath. 'Why don't you stand up and fight the giant?' asked David to which his brothers replied 'Don't you see, he is too big to hit.' But

David had a different perspective. He said *'No, he is not too big to hit, he is too big to miss.'* And then with a slingshot, he kills the Goliath. It was the same giant. However, other people focused only on obstacles but David saw the opportunity. While others were afraid of the size of the Goliath, David saw Goliath's size as an opportunity and exploited that opportunity in his and his countrymen's favour.'

Ajay was now realising the importance of perspective. He now understood how by changing one's focus from obstacles to opportunity, one can achieve his/her desired goal.

'Another key difference between the thought process of Rich and Poor people is that *Rich people focus on what they want while poor people focus on what they don't want,'* said Manisha. 'Again the Universal Law states 'what you focus on expands.' Because rich people focus on the opportunities in everything, opportunities abound for them. On the other hand, because poor people focus on what they don't want which are obstacles, risks and difficulties, obstacles abound for them.'

'Rich people also understand that you can never know all the information beforehand. Whenever they see an opportunity, they prepare themselves for that opportunity in a short time and then take the plunge. They believe in getting ready for the best in as minimum time as possible, take actions; and then correct along the way. They know that one of the ways people learn to do right is by doing it wrong and then learning the mistake and moving forward.'

'Poor people on the other hand, keep on preparing themselves for the opportunity for weeks, months or years. By the time they consider themselves to be prepared, the opportunity usually disappears. Most of the poor people practice procrastination by hiding behind high sounding words, saying 'I am analysing' and six months later they are still analysing. What they don't realise is that they are suffering from a disease called *Paralysis by Analysis* and if they don't overcome this disease they will never succeed.'

'It's actually foolish to think that you can know everything that may happen in the future. It's delusional to believe that you can prepare for every circumstance that might occur someday and protect yourself from it during your journey. Getting yourself prepared for the entire journey is like waiting for all the traffic signals from Bengaluru to Mysore to be green before you switch on your car. It doesn't happen that way. You should start your journey, make wrong turns, ask for the correct path during your journey, correct yourself along the way and then only you will be able to reach your goal. Life doesn't travel in perfectly straight lines. It moves more like a winding river. More often than not, you can only see up to the next bend and only when you reach that next turn can you see more.'

'Remember opportunity doesn't wait for you to get ready, neither does it allow you to finish certain tasks after which you can grab that opportunity. Opportunity is a like a goddess and she showers her blessings equally among everyone. She is very fair in her approach and does not discriminate among people. However, it is people who don't accept her blessings rather continue to curse their bad luck throughout their life. Those who take actions when they see an opportunity can bask under the glory of the goddess.'

'Let me give you a real life example of how successful and rich people thinks when it comes to opportunity and obstacles and how they focus on their strength rather than wasting time on analysing the obstacles.' Manisha then got up from her seat and opened an old edition of *The Economic Times* and handed the paper to Ajay pointing at a particular article.[4] The article read:

Unfazed by Jio Entry: Voda's Sood

'Vodafone India is prepared for increased competition post Reliance Jio's entry,' said CEO Sunil Sood. Instead of paying attention to rivals, Sood told ET, the telco would focus on its own operations and strength.

'You know, what are the saddest words in life?' asked Manisha after Ajay handed her the newspaper.

'No idea,' said Ajay.

'The saddest words in life are: 'It might have been....' 'I should have done that....' 'I could have....' 'I wish I could reverse the time and take actions....' and 'If only I had given a little extra....' So if you want to succeed, if you want to create wealth and if you want to be happy then always remember that you never put yourself in situations where you have to utter those words. Remember, *a small step is much more powerful than the mightiest intentions.*'

Difference #3
Rich People are students throughout their life.
Poor People's learning stops after formal education.

Manisha then rang the bell and asked the office boy to bring two cups of tea for them. 'Now let us come to the last point of our discussion,' said Manisha taking a sip from her

---

[4]Taken from *The Economic Times*, Bengaluru edition dated 31st Aug 2015.

cup. 'This is one of the most important lessons you would learn before you start learning the rules of *wealth creation and accumulation* from Vinay.'

'And what is that?' asked Ajay.

'It is called the art of continuous learning. *Rich people are students throughout their life while for most of the poor and middle-class people, their learning stops after their school/college.*'

'Now that Kiara is almost a year old, she must be crawling' asked Manisha.

'Yes, she crawls and sometimes we help her walk but right now she cannot walk on her own.'

'Do you know kids are the best learners? First they listen when their parents speak to them and then they learn to speak. Then they learn to use their hands and legs. They fall a lot in their process of learning to walk but since they see everyone around walking, they are very eager to walk and run and they ultimately learn to walk with their persistence.'

'I know that. But how is it related with our present discussion?'

'Ever wondered, if kids when they have learnt crawling think that they do not need to learn anymore, that they know everything; what would happen to them?'

'I guess they would restrict themselves to crawling. They would never learn walking and running.'

'This also happens to poor and middle-class people. Once they are out of school and college, most of them think that after their school and college – their learning is over and they know everything now. They keep themselves contended with crawling because most of them have never seen anybody in their family walking and running. They think that it is how a person leads his life – that crawling is the way of life.'

'There may be few exceptional persons, who despite coming from a family where nobody has learnt to walk and run sees other people running in full speed and then they desire to become like them. And when their desires turn into commitment, they learn the process and method of walking and very soon they also start running. But majority of the poor and middle-class people are content with crawling. They are satisfied with their life and with their ability to make a living for themselves thinking it would be too much pain to walk and run. Also they fear a lot of falling and that is why they prefer crawling. *They have the mindset that if they crawl; chance of them falling is nil but if they try to learn to walk and run they might fall. The fear of falling far outweighs the joy of walking and running for them.*'

'Rich people on the other hand believe that school and college has just given them the foundation and platform,' continued Manisha. 'For them real learning happens from their life experiences and by observing and reading life experiences of others. They understand that only with learning you can grow both as an individual and as a contributing member of the society. They are not content with simply making a living. They want to live their life fully and they know that it is achievable; only thing is that they need to keep their eyes, ears and mind open all throughout their life.'

'Do you know, when somebody stops growing?' asked Manisha.

'It is when they stop learning.'

'Correct. The physical growth of a person stops at the age of 16–18 years. However, God has gifted us with an ability to grow mentally, emotionally and intellectually all throughout our life. But most of the people are not aware of this gift.

Once the sense of ego and self-justification settles in, most of the people start proving to themselves that they already know everything. And *when you believe that you know everything, you stop learning and you stop growing.* Whenever you say that you know everything, you are actually shutting down the opportunity to learn something new. However, when you say I don't know that thing then you open an opportunity for yourself to learn and grow.'

'Do you know why Poor and Middle-class people always struggle throughout their life?' asked Manisha.

Ajay shrugged his shoulder in ignorance fully aware that Manisha would help him learn something new.

'It is because they don't understand the importance of a simple fact, i.e. if you're not really rich and really happy, there's a very good chance that you are missing something about creating wealth and happiness and that you still have few things to learn about money, success and life. Remember, if you keep doing what you've always done, you'll keep getting what you've always got.'

'The only way to make money is to learn how to play the money game. You need to learn the skills and strategies to accelerate your income, to manage money and to invest it effectively. The definition of insanity is doing the same thing over and over and expecting different results. Stop doing what is not working and look for something new. See, if what you've been doing was working, you'd already be rich and happy, but if it is not the case then it means that you need to learn something which you have been missing till now.'

'Remember, achieving success and creating and accumulating wealth is a learnable skill. You can learn to succeed at anything.

If you want to be a great cricketer, you can learn how to be one. If you want to be a great violin player, you can learn how to be one. If you want to be truly happy, you can learn how to be a wealthy person. And if you want to be rich, you can learn how to be wealthy person. It doesn't matter where you are right now. It doesn't matter where you are starting from. What matters is that you are willing to learn. No one comes out of their mother's womb as a financial genius. Every rich person learned how to succeed at the money game and so can you. *If they can do it, so can you.*'

'Warren Buffet, the self-made billionaire and one of the richest man on Earth is a personification of the principle of 'art of continuous learning.' He says: '*I read 500 pages of book/article/ report every day. That's how knowledge builds up, like compound interest.*' Daily reading is a key habit for him as he seeks new information and opportunities. He reads far and wide: multiple newspapers each day, large numbers of financial reports on potential investments and books. Over time the knowledge he learns compounds and yields greater insights that helps him in his investment decisions. Most of the rich people also follow the same principle. They read, read and read. It's their curiosity that drives them. They simply have to know. They constantly seek new ways to become better. *While Poor and Middle-class people view reading books as some leisure-time luxury, rich people consider it to be a necessity because it helps them to grow.*'

'I understand that continuous learning is very important in order to be successful and becoming rich. But how do we get to learn? I mean whom shall we approach to learn about money, its management and investments?' asked Ajay.

'You have raised a very pertinent question,' said Manisha

with a smile. 'While continuous learning is important but from whom you are learning is even more important. *Generally, rich people take advice from people who are richer than they are, but poor people take advice from their friends, relatives and unsolicited financial advisors, brokers and agents who are just as broke as they are.'*

'I didn't understand this unsolicited financial advisors part,' said Ajay looking slightly confused.

'Have you received calls from the so called financial advisors from various banks/brokerage houses claiming themselves to be experts in investments and who explain you various investment options and ask you to invest in some or the other investment tools?' asked Manisha.

'Yes, I receive many such calls on regular intervals. And there are instances when I get multiple calls in a single day.'

'So, have you invested upon the advice of those unsolicited calls in any of those investment tools?'

'Yes, I have invested in a few of them.'

'And how has been your experience? Have you made any reasonable gains from those investments?'

'No. In fact, in few of these cases I have made losses,' said Ajay with a sad face.

'As I had predicted,' said Manisha. 'Suppose, you are looking for a job in one of the top software companies say Google, Microsoft or Intel.'

Ajay felt uncomfortable on hearing about seeking job opportunities but controlled his emotion for he knew that Manisha didn't mean to hurt him.

'When you make calls to these companies...' continued Manisha.

Hi Sir, I am a potential employee. I come from a reputed institute with nearly 8 years of experience in software product development. I have domain knowledge of networking and telecommunication. I can greatly enhance the output of the department in which I'm placed. I am hard working, smart, efficient and presentable. Also, I am a great team player. When do you want me to start?

What are the chances of you being hired after you make such calls to your dream companies?'

'Nil,' said Ajay.

'Then why do you hire your financial advisor after he or she makes a cold call to you. Why do you put your hard-earned money in the hands of those who just have made a phone call to you? Would a good company ever hire a key employee without doing a serious background check and an in-depth interview? No! Yet most people, even those with high incomes, hire financial advisors after obtaining little or no background information about these "employment candidates,"' said Manisha.

'But I am not hiring any employee. I am just doing some investments with the person who called me.'

'Why do companies hire people?'

'To manage their operations,' replied Ajay.

'Why does each and every company have a dedicated finance team?'

'To manage its finances.'

'Similarly, you hire your financial advisor to get your finances in proper order. So that they can help you manage your money and investments. Just like a company pays its employee some salaries for their service, you also pay commission and fees to your financial advisor for their service. And hence you should view all financial advisors, insurance agents, bankers, brokerage house who solicit you as client merely as applicants who are seeking job opportunities from you. And just like best companies hire best employees, you should also choose the best financial advisors/agents by carrying out due diligence on them; like what is their past record, who are their present clients and what is their expertise. You can try to get the correct financial advisors through references from your friends and/or relatives who had good experience from them in the past. Always remember that *your ability to hire high-grade financial advisors, real estate brokers and agents is directly related to your chances to accumulate wealth.*'

'Let me tell you one of my personal experiences that I had with one of the Wealth Managers from an MNC bank,' continued Manisha. 'He was constantly following me and was asking me to invest with him. One day he calls me and said, "I am very good at investing money for my clients and have over ten years of experience in wealth management. My clientele includes many High Networth Individuals (HNIs) of the cities. You please send me your financial statements including your last year income tax return and then I will advise you about the optimal portfolio distribution for your income level."

'I listened to him patiently and then said, 'So you're really good at investments and managing money for your clients. Then you must be very good at managing your own money as well. Why don't you send me a copy of your personal income tax returns for the last few years and the list of investment securities that you have had in your own portfolio for the last two years. If you made more money than I did from investments, I'll invest with you.' The man was in shock as he informed me that it was against his company's policy to share their individual statements with clients. Then I told him either he accepts what I am proposing or better do not disturb me again. After that incident, I didn't get any call from any representatives of that bank.'

'If you want to learn how to drive a car, would you hire a guide who knows every technical details of a car like its accelerator, its horse power, its torque but has never driven a car; or would it be smarter to find someone who actually knows about car driving? Just as there is a way to drive a car, there are proven routes and strategies for creating high income, fast financial freedom and wealth. You just have to choose the correct guide, coach and advisor.'

'I see your point. It's not just continuous learning but from whom we learn and take advice is all the more important,' said Ajay.

'Yes,' said Manisha. 'We live in the information age. Information is priceless. A good financial advisor or broker provides you with information, as well as take the time to educate you. So, try to spend time to find a good financial advisor for yourself.'

Their conversation was broken by the ringing of Manisha's phone. It was her husband who informed her that he would not be coming to office; rather he would be going to home directly after the meeting with the client. Manisha asked how the meeting went, to which he said that he would discuss with her in detail when they meet at home.

'So, how do you feel now?' asked Manisha.

'I feel financially baptised,' said Ajay with a smile. 'I learnt so many things today from you. I am totally in control with myself now. All thanks to you.'

'All thanks to Vinay for teaching us how to think like rich and successful people,' said Manisha. 'But don't be overwhelmed.

Your journey has just started. Vinay will now tell you about the *'Scrolls of Wealth Creation and Accumulation.'* I am pretty sure, once your journey is over, you will not be the same person. You would become a better Ajay climbing on the stairs of wealth and success.'

Ajay smiled and then both of them got up to go home.

Part II

THE ACTION

Five

KNOW YOUR BOOKS

Next week when Ajay went to meet Vinay at his home in the evening, Vinay was busy playing with his kids. Seeing Ajay, Vinay immediately got up and went to his room. When he returned, he had a paper in his hand. Meanwhile Ananya, Vinay's wife had prepared tea with some eats for them. After finishing the tea and relishing the hot *pakodas*, both of them then left for the nearby park to stroll off the extra calories.

'So, how was your meeting with Manisha?' asked Vinay.

'It was amazing, I must say. After meeting with her, I realised what differentiates a winner from a loser and how rich and successful people use their thought process in their favour. It was remarkable. I feel more liberated, free to go after my goal; I feel Financially Baptised now,' said Ajay with a smile.

'Great! So, how's your job hunt going on?'

'I have applied in a few companies. Day before yesterday I got a call from one of the companies. It was the basic Telephonic Interview. I think, I have cleared that as they have scheduled for a face-to-face interview next week,' replied Ajay.

'Good. You will get through it.'

'Can't say as of now. Presently, the market is lively for job seekers. Also, there are too many people out in the market looking for jobs. I need to prepare myself better to get through the process. I need to focus on my strengths, on the opportunities and not just on the obstacles.'

Seeing the change in Ajay's outlook and the fact that he was taking responsibility for himself Vinay spoke 'Looks like you have learnt your lessons well from Manisha.'

Vinay then took out a piece of paper from his pocket. Before giving it to Ajay he told him about the letters that his father used to send him. It was these letters which helped Vinay gain knowledge and wisdom about money and how it increases in the hands of those who knows and understands the rules of *Wealth Creation and Accumulation* and abide by those rules. He also told Ajay that he has kept these letters preserved and often read them to keep his wisdom about money and wealth intact.

'Though these letters were given to me by my father, I think it can be read by anyone who has a deep desire to accumulate wealth and excel in his life. Now that you are ready to learn the lessons, I will hand over to you one letter at a time to read and grasp the true meaning of it,' said Vinay.

Sure. I am too eager to learn the wisdom that Uncle has shared with you,' Ajay sounded excited.

Vinay then handed over the letter to Ajay and sat in a nearby bench in the park observing Ajay reading the letter.

Dear Son,

The first and foremost thing that you should do before you start earning money is to understand how the money flows into your hand and how it leaves. When you earn your income through your work and skills, money flows into your hand. It fills your wallet. And then money flows out from your hand, i.e. it leaves your wallet when you purchase items for your living. These items may be necessary goods such as food, clothing etc. or it may be luxury goods. Then what is left in your wallet is your savings. In simple words: Income less Expense is your Savings.

Having understood the concepts of income and expense, you should also understand the importance of Assets and Liabilities. Assets are something which you own and which brings money into your wallet, just like income does. And liabilities are those which you owe to someone and which take out money from your wallet, just like your expenses.

I would also like you to know that there is a relationship between your Income–Expense statement and Asset–Liability Statement. That I would leave it to you to explore for it is in exploration and desire to find something that people learn the most and keep the wisdom learnt for the longest period of time.

Lovingly yours,
Ram Prasad

Ajay read the letter again, trying to understand what Vinay's father was trying to convey to him. He then looked at Vinay who was silently observing him smiling. Ajay tried to smile too but his mind was busy in understanding the true meaning of the letter. He read it again and then folded the letter and gave it back to Vinay.

'So, how do you feel now after reading the letter?' Vinay asked.

'I feel, I have been too ignorant,' replied Ajay.

'To be ignorant is not anyone's fault; but choosing to remain ignorant will definitely lead to a downfall. Bill Gates, the founder of Microsoft has rightly said '*If you are born poor it's not your fault. But if you die poor, it's your fault.*' Now that you have chosen to gain financial wisdom, I assure you my friend, from here on you will only climb steps towards success, towards wealth creation and accumulation – towards happiness,' said Vinay.

Ajay smiled on hearing wise words from Vinay. He then spoke, 'It's been more than eight years since we graduated from our college, but it seems I don't know much about finance and its technicalities. Though I have been good at numbers and have done pretty well in the subject of Maths in both school and college days, I feel that I need to have some knowledge of finance, stock market etc. to understand the world of finance. I read the letter thrice; however, I am not able to comprehend words like Asset and Liabilities. Also I couldn't exactly understand the relationship between Income–Expense statement and Asset–Liability statement that Uncle was hinting in the letter. If you can explain it in simple words to me, then I would be able to grasp its meaning.'

'Definitely my friend,' said Vinay. 'But before I explain, I want you to know that understanding the basic principles of finance is very easy. Finance is not about the numbers and mathematics. Numbers alone don't tell you anything. Many people want to avoid topics related to personal finance, savings and investments because they think that it's all about numbers and that you need to understand stock market, money market etc. Nothing can be farther from the truth.'

'*Finance is nothing but common sense,*' continued Vinay. 'It has been there since time immemorial. Even our great kings like Samudragupta, Asoka and Akbar had a finance minister and treasurer who used to look after the finances of their kingdoms. People used to discuss finance even before modern mathematics and statistics were developed. Remember, there was no Regression Analysis or Standard Deviation and no Fundamental or Technical Analysis during 200BC or even during 1500AD. Yet people used to discuss about income, savings, investments and taxation during that period as well.'

'Even in our present time, if you look at Arundhati Bhattacharya who is the Chairman and Managing Director of the biggest bank of India – State Bank of India – she doesn't have any coveted or prestigious financial degree. She has her BA and MA degrees in English Literature from Jadavpur University, Kolkata. She doesn't have any degree in Economics, Finance or Mathematics, yet she is the Chairman and MD of the biggest bank of the country. So, the notion that you need to be good at mathematics and numbers to understand finance is entirely wrong. *To understand your finances, you just need to focus on the flow of money and once you realise the nature of its flow and the rules governing its movement, then you will understand what has been stopping you from becoming rich.*'

Vinay then explained to Ajay that just like a company has its Profit and Loss Account and the Balance Sheet, an individual also has similar books. An individual's Profit and Loss Account is nothing but his monthly income and expense also called Income–expense account and his Balance Sheet is his Assets and Liabilities. And just like the balance sheet of a company tells the true picture of the financial health of the company, the individual's financial statement also tell how well that person is doing financially. Vinay also explained that just like a company aims to be a profitable unit and make as much profit as possible, an individual should also try to make him/herself a profitable entity.

'Isn't everybody a profitable entity? After all, everyone is making an income for his family,' asked Ajay with surprise.

'That is what most people don't understand,' Vinay remarked. 'It is not your income which makes you a profitable entity. It is your income less your expense, i.e. your savings, which makes you a profitable person. *Wealth is not the same as income.* Income is just one part of your wealth creation. Dr Thomas Stanley, the famous author and lecturer has rightly said that '*If you make a good income each year and spend it all, you are not getting wealthier. You are just living high. Wealth is what you accumulate and not what you earn.*'

Ajay realised since the beginning of his career he has been living high. He had bought everything upscale and now he doesn't have much savings left in his bank account. And in the name of investments he has just his own house which he fears would be taken over by the Bank if he is not able to make his payments on time.

'Do you know that people of Texas, USA have a specific term for those who spends heavily and is unable to create assets for themselves,' continued Vinay. 'They call those people as **Big Hat, No Cattle**. What essentially it means is that people who spend heavily have a very big hat to show off but does not have any cattle – that is they don't have any material substance to back them. Essentially, they are hollow spheres with a golden paint on the surface. They will make a lot of sound just like a hollow sphere does by splurging their money and purchasing high end items to suit their so called upscale and high societal status but they don't realise that inside they are empty and hollow; without any substance.' Vinay paused for some time to let the idea sink in to Ajay's mind and then continued, '*To become wealthy one should aim to become a solid sphere.*'

'People too often spend their entire income on upgrading their lifestyles. They would purchase high end consumer goods mostly on credit and then spend their entire earnings for the next few months just to clear those credit card bills. Whenever you are tempted to splurge your entire earnings on upgrading your lifestyle just remember what Jim Rohn has to say – '*If your outgo exceeds your income, your upkeep will become your downfall.*''

Vinay then proceeded to explain the difference between surplus and deficit and how it leads to creation of Assets and Liabilities respectively. He told that when an individual's income exceeds his expense, it leads to a surplus and then this surplus from his Profit and Loss account goes to his Balance Sheet to create Assets. And when an individual's income is less than his expenses, it creates a deficit and this deficit then has to be met through an increase in Liabilities.

'Let me explain this through a diagram which will help you in understanding this very simple concept,' said Vinay taking out a piece of paper and pen from his pocket. Ajay was now sitting along with Vinay and was observing very carefully whatever Vinay was explaining to him.

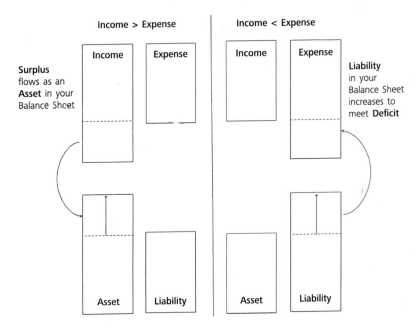

'There is a relationship between your income–expense statement and asset–liability statement. Your income–expense statement is a process which creates the asset and liability boxes. It is your asset-liability statement which reflects what you truly are and your income–expense statement shows how you are managing your money. The better you are at managing your income–expense statement, the better your asset–liability statement will look like and the better your asset–liability statement is, the wealthier you become.'

'Most of the people focus only on income in their desire to become rich but they do not know that income is just one of the factors required to become rich. You have to combine Savings and Investments with your Income to create wealth and become rich. Remember, *a person is not called rich by his income, he becomes rich when he has a strong asset column in his balance sheet.*'

'So as you see, whenever there is surplus it creates assets for you. Again, you must notice from the diagram that it is not the Income but the Savings, the Surplus which is going to Balance Sheet to create Assets. But, if you end up having deficit, i.e. your income is not able to take care of your expense then what do you do? You borrow either from your friend, through credit card or through bank loan which leads to creating liabilities for you,' said Vinay giving the piece of the paper with diagrams to Ajay so that he can have a better look.

Ajay after carefully observing the diagram and relating it with whatever Vinay told him spoke, 'So whenever my income is greater than expense, I become a profitable entity by creating surplus and then this surplus creates assets for me. But whenever my expense is greater than income, I become a loss making entity and the deficit in the income has to be met through increase in liability such as Bank loans, Credit Cards etc.'

'Correct,' said Vinay with a smile.

'However, I have one doubt,' spoke Ajay. 'I read about Asset and Liabilities everywhere. Even in newspaper, they discuss about assets and liabilities. I tried to read it on internet also but couldn't exactly get the true meaning.'

'The definition of assets and liabilities that you read in books and internet is purely academic. These definitions are used by Bankers, Accountants and Lawyers and that is why these sound too technical and are used to confuse normal people like you and me,' said Vinay. 'Thankfully, my father didn't go to school and college to learn about these. He understood the true meaning of assets and liabilities through his life experiences and then developed a simple definition which has helped me a lot. He used to say *'Assets are items which you own and which brings money to your wallet and Liabilities are items which you owe to someone else and which takes away money from your wallet*[5].'

Vinay then took out another sheet and drew a diagram.

'Always remember that Assets behave similar to your Income in terms of fattening your wallet by bringing money into it and making you rich; and liabilities behave similar to expenses since both make your wallet thin by taking money out of it. *So if you want to become rich, either you need to increase your income or create assets for yourself. And I will tell you from my personal*

---

[5]Robert T Kiyoski has the best quote on Assets and Liabilities. He says, 'An Asset puts money in my pocket. A liability takes money out of my pocket.' The definition has been slightly modified to make it easy to picturise and understand.

experience that creating assets from your already earned income is much easier than increasing your existing income. Further, just like Income less expense is your savings similarly when you subtract Liabilities from your Assets then you get your *Net Worth*. Your Net Worth which is the present value of your Assets less Liabilities is the true measure of your wealth as it reflects your true possessions and show how rich or poor you are.'

'So, the true indicator of anyone whether he is wealthy or not is his Net Worth; and not his income?' asked Ajay.

'Yes,' replied Vinay. 'To become wealthy you need to create assets and minimise liabilities. And this can be done only when you start creating surplus for you and your family so that you can put your savings into rightful assets. *Having a strong net worth will not only allow you to live your life as per your dreams, it will also give you confidence in every endeavour of yours.* Some wise man has rightly said '*It is in favour of man to have surplus and assets by his side; for a man with a surplus controls his circumstances and the man without a surplus is controlled by his circumstances.*"

'You will never see a wealthy person with liabilities exceeding his assets because liabilities will never make you rich. It will pull you down. It will lead to draining of your money from your wallet in the form of interest payment which will make you poor. Rather, it is assets which make people wealthy and rich. Assets will help you generate further income in the form of interest income, dividend and rental income which will fatten your wallet and make you rich.'

Vinay then took out another piece of paper and drew two flow diagrams.

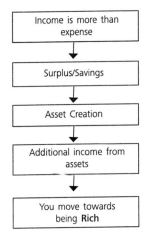

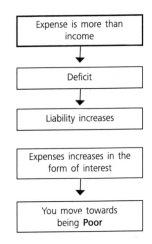

Ajay was now starting to realise the importance of understanding one's books. He now knew why he had fallen into debt trap despite earning a handsome income. All his life he had been running after every hike in his salary, he had been working hard to get that coveted promotion; little did he know that it is not one's income but his/her savings that leads an individual towards the path of wealth and happiness. He also realised how he had been increasing his liabilities in the form of credit card bills, EMIs for his home loan and car loan and how most of his income was going towards meeting the interest and principal payment for these loans. *This cycle of increasing his liabilities and paying interest and principal payment from his income had never allowed him to create surplus and that is why he didn't have any substantial asset in his or his family's name.*

Spend More Time Managing Your Money

Seeing Ajay lost in his thoughts, Vinay asked him how much time he spends every month on an average to manage his money.

Ajay thought for some time and then replied, 'Well, after making the EMI payments for my home and car as also paying the necessary utility bills, there is hardly any money left to manage after the 5th of every month.'

'I am not asking that. I am asking how much time you spend every month for planning your investment decisions. How much time do you give to analyse various investment options and then to invest your money? How much time do you give to allocate your earned money to various baskets like investment basket, expense basket, and indulgence basket among others?'

'I don't understand what you are talking about,' said Ajay.

Vinay then took out another piece of paper, drew a diagram and gave it to Ajay.

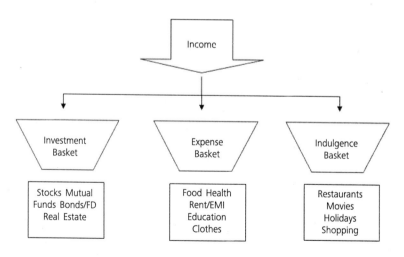

'Every month we get our salary or income from our business and then that money flows into these three baskets. The examples that I have mentioned in the diagram is just an indicative list to help you understand the importance of the three baskets. Now tell me how much time you give every month to decide what part of your salary/income goes in to one of the three baskets?'

'Like I said before, after making the EMI payment for my home and car and paying the necessary utility bills, I don't have much money left to manage them,' replied Ajay.

Vinay smiled on hearing Ajay's response. He then said, 'Everybody allocates their money in one of the basket either consciously or unconsciously. In your case, you are allocating money in your expense basket unconsciously. You do not decide how much of your money should go into one of the baskets. You are simply putting them as per the demand of your bank or as per your needs and desires. And when you allocate your money into various baskets unconsciously, then it is called mismanaging your money.'

'On the other hand, if you allocate your money into various baskets consciously, then it is called managing your money. If you see the difference between the two, it is not about the amount of money that goes into various baskets that we are discussing. It is about putting it consciously or unconsciously.'

'Now, one major difference between rich and poor people is that *Rich people choose to allocate their money into different baskets consciously and poor people allocate it unconsciously.* And the advantage of allocating money consciously into various baskets is that you are in control of your hard earned money. It is you, who decides how much of your money should go into which basket. While if you allocate money unconsciously then it is not you; but your money, which decides where should it go.'

'It has been proven statistically[6] that people who go on to become rich and accumulate wealth have the habit of allocating nearly twice the number of hours per month to planning their financial investments compared to the people who do not become rich. There is a strong correlation between investment planning and wealth accumulation. *Rich people spend more time in deciding how much money from their income should go to which basket.* They spend more time consulting professional investment advisors; searching for right investment tools and less time worrying about their financial well-being.'

'The poor and middle-class on the other hand have no or very little clue on how much of their income is going into which basket. They mostly are anxious about their financial straitjacket, when they accept they are poor and they don't have money. And what happens if you spend much of your time worrying about a lot of issues that concern you? You will spend less time taking action to solve those problems.'

'It all boils down to this simple fact: *the single biggest difference between financial success and financial failure is how well you manage your money. To master the game of money, you should learn to manage the money.* Rich people are good at managing their money. They manage their money very well. Middle-class and Poor people don't give time to manage their money and as a result they become good in mismanaging their money.'

---

[6]Based on the research/survey/seminar conducted by Thomas J Stanley, PhD and William D Danko, PhD.

'Will not managing the money restrict my freedom? Will it not deprive me from enjoying the luxuries that I could indulge?' asked Ajay.

'Managing money does not restrict your freedom – on the contrary it promotes it. Managing your money allows you to eventually create financial freedom so that you never have to work against your wishes; so that you don't need to work to pay your EMI and monthly bills. Actually you can choose to work based on your choices. Having money frees you from the financial pressures; it gives you the freedom of choice. There is a difference between making a living and making a life. With wealth in your hand you can make your own life. To me, that's real freedom.'

'Let me give you an example which you come across every day. Suppose you are going to your office on a Monday morning and you come across a traffic signal which is being controlled by a Traffic Police. Now what does Traffic Policeman do? He manages the traffic by allowing vehicles from only one side of the crossroads to go at a time while stopping vehicles from other three roads. The vehicles from other roads move when their turn comes – when Traffic Police presses green button for them to move. In this scenario everybody gets their turn to cross the signal and movement of the traffic is smooth.'

'Now suppose you come across the same signal the next day. However, this time there is no Traffic Policeman and neither is the Traffic signal working. What happens then? Will you be able to move smoothly? No, because there will be a commotion. Every vehicle would want to pass the signal by one way or the other and this will result into chaos, a perfect jam and you will get struck cursing the traffic for getting you late for your office.'

'While in the first scenario, where Traffic Police is managing the traffic you don't have the freedom to move as per your wish. You move only when you see green light in front of you. You may say your freedom is getting restricted. But in reality, it is this restriction which helps you cross the signal smoothly and on time. On the other hand in the second scenario, you have complete freedom to move. But are you able to move? No. Why does it happen so? It is because there is nobody to manage the traffic.'

'Similarly in the case of money, if you manage your money well you move towards your freedom; the freedom to choose your work/job as per your liking, the freedom to take leave from your work whenever you wish, the freedom to pursue your hobby and passion. And if you don't manage your money well, you will always be controlled by money. Lack of money in your bank account will always make you sad; will always compel you to work hard so that your job is safe even if you may not like doing it. Lack of money will create a fear in you – the fear of not being able to pay the bills, the fear of being fired and the fear of not getting hike in your salaries.'

Ajay thought for some time and realised how managing the money actually promotes the freedom. However he had another query running in his mind and he spoke, 'Isn't it because Rich people have so much money with them that they need to manage their money and hire professional investment advisors? I don't have much money with me so what shall I manage? Shouldn't I start managing when I have money with me?'

'You are looking from the wrong end of telescope, my friend,' said Vinay. 'Rather than saying that 'when I have plenty of money, I'll begin to manage it,' the reality is 'when I begin to manage it, I'll have plenty of money.' Remember, not everyone is born rich. But people who on their effort become rich are those who have been good at managing their money since beginning.'

'Saying that 'I'll start managing my money as soon as I have plenty of money with me' is like an overweight person saying 'I'll start exercising and dieting as soon as I lose ten kg.' You can't lose weight until you start exercising. Similarly, you can't become wealthy until you start managing your money. First you start properly handling the money you have, then you'll have more money to handle. It's all about habit. Once you get into the habit of managing your money then it doesn't matter with how much money you start with or what impact it would have. What matters is you get into the right habit. Remember, *money is not permanent; your habit remains permanent with you and even if you lose money then with your habit and discipline you can get it back.*'

'I too started with a small amount. Six years ago, I used to save only ₹4,000 every month and then used to manage them properly. And then I got into this habit of managing money. And today, my habit remains the same; however the number of zeros has changed in the amount of money that I manage with the time. Remember, we are creatures of habit and therefore habit of managing the money is more important than the amount.'

'Let me give you one example,' Vinay paused for some time and then asked 'How old is Kiara?'

'She is almost a year old.'

'Well at this age, she wouldn't be eating ice cream. But four years later, she would definitely become fond of ice cream. Suppose when she is five; you are walking along a street with Kiara. You come across an ice cream parlour and go inside. You get Kiara a single scoop ice cream cone because the parlour doesn't have any cups. As the two of you walk outside, you notice the cone wobbling in Kiara's tiny hands and, all of a sudden, plop. The ice cream falls out of the cone onto the pavement.'

'Kiara begins to cry. So you go back into the parlour and just as you're about to order for the second time, Kiara notices a colourful sign with an attractive picture of the 'triple scooper' cone. Kiara points to the picture and excitedly screams, 'I want that one! I want that ice cream with three scoops and cherries!'

'Now here's the question. Being the kind, loving and generous father that you are, would you go ahead and get Kiara the triple scooper? Your initial response might be 'sure.' However, when considering the question a little more deeply, you might reply, 'No.' Because why would you want to set Kiara up to fail? She couldn't even handle a single scoop, how could she possibly handle a triple scoop?[7]

'The same holds true when it comes to the universe and you. We live in a kind and loving universe and the rule is: *Until you show you can handle what you've got, you won't get any more!* The universe watches us and entrusts us with more money only when we have managed our money well. It's simple, first you prove and then you get.

'It's just like assigning a task to one of your subordinates. You wouldn't assign a challenging task to him until he has proven that he can handle it. If he has failed earlier in some simple task then you wouldn't entrust him with the new task. Rather, you

---

[7]The example has been taken from the book, *Secrets of the Millionaire Mind,* where the author Harv Eker has beautifully explained why it is important to manage what you already have before you expect to receive more.

would look for someone on whom you have confidence and you are sure that he/she can manage it and deliver it on time.

'Rich people know and understand this fact and hence abide by them to become richer. Planning and managing the finances is one of the key ingredients in building wealth. Most of the rich people have a regimented planning schedule. Each week, each month and each year they plan their investments. Middle-class on the other hand plan their investments only in the month of January and February when they need to submit proof for availing tax benefits. Here again, their primary motive is to save tax and not to make their wealth appreciate in value and hence chances of putting their money into wrong investment tools is very high. During these two months, the time spent by the middle-class people in planning their investments and managing their money is much more than the time spent by the Rich people as Rich people would have already made proper investments for availing tax benefit at the start of the financial year and hence do not have to rush to various financial planners and brokers at the end of the year.

'This behaviour of middle-class is very much similar to an overweight person who occasionally starves himself to reach his ideal weight. But more often than not, they regain all the weight they lost and more. To have the ideal weight, you need to have the habit of exercising daily for small duration. You cannot gain your dream physique and figure by working out eight hours every day for a week. However, if you exercise one hour every day for the next fifty-six days, you will definitely move closer to your dream physique.'

Ajay now had understood the importance of managing his money. He promised himself that no matter what is the amount, he would get into the habit of managing his money. Also, he would give time for planning and managing his investments every month rather than wait for the year end.

The sun had almost set and birds were returning to their nests to feed their younger ones. The chirping of the birds was all around the park. Ajay; however was feeling a sublime peace in that evening noise. Most of the people had already left the park for their home and it was time for the two friends to return to theirs.

Six

PAY YOURSELF FIRST

It was November 1st – the *Karnataka Rajyotsava* day – and being a public holiday Ajay excused himself for a longer sleep than his usual routine. Priya had already got up and was preparing breakfast for Kiara, who was playing with her toys in her cradle. After feeding Kiara and changing her diapers, Priya was anxiously waiting for her maid to come so that she can go and take bath. Seeing no signs of her, Priya tried calling her maid and when there was no response for the fifth time, she got herself busy in cleaning the utensils.

Ajay woke up on hearing the cries of Kiara. She had puked everything her mother had fed her half an hour ago. He tried calling Priya from his bed but when she did not come to his rescue, he got up and took Kiara in his arms. She had made a complete mess of her new dress and was now crying furiously.

'What happened? Why is Kiara crying?' Priya shouted from the kitchen.

'She has puked everything,' replied Ajay searching for a new dress for his daughter in the wardrobe.

'First change her dress; it's on the fourth shelf of the left wardrobe,' came the booming voice from the kitchen.

'Yeah, that's what I am doing.'

After changing Kiara's dress, Ajay sang a lullaby to her and played with her. He then put the soiled dress in the bathroom. Wondering what Priya is doing in the kitchen for such a long time, he put Kiara on the bed, put two pillows on either side of her and left to see Priya.

'What happened? Isn't the maid coming today?'

'Maharaniji is on leave today. Of course without informing me,' replied Priya without looking at him.

'Did you call her to see whether she is coming or not?'

'Do you think that I would be cleaning this stuff without checking with her? I called her but she didn't answer the call.'

Knowing that Priya was angry, Ajay went close to her to hold her from behind. Then he gave a peck on her neck. 'Don't be angry. Once you clean these, I will put them in the cabinet,' Ajay tried his best to extend help from his side.

Once she was done with the utensils, Priya went to the bedroom to see Kiara who had fallen asleep by now and then proceeded to the bathroom. Ajay, after finishing his part went to rest on his sofa with the morning newspaper in his hand. While browsing through the news, he suddenly remembered that it was November 1st and that he must have received his last month's salary yesterday. He picked his smart phone from his study table and tried to switch it on. Seeing that the battery had completely drained out, he connected his mobile to the charger and in the meanwhile opened his laptop to see his bank account statement.

The salary was credited to his account and Ajay knew that it was the second last payslip from his current organisation. He had to find another job within a month now. He then checked his Credit Card bill and home loan EMI that needed to be paid by fifth of every month and was relieved on seeing that he could make EMI payments and other bills for another five months with his current account balance. While he was making payment for his EMI and other utility bills, the door bell rang. He got up from the sofa and went to the main door.

'Vinay! What a pleasant surprise. Come inside,' Ajay exclaimed seeing Vinay standing at the door.

'I hope I didn't disturb you,' said Vinay as he walked in.

'No. Not at all. Come in. Have a seat,' Ajay said, removing towels and other dresses from the sofa.

'I am going to my company's headquarters in the USA for three months,' said Vinay. 'While I was packing my bag, I remembered that I needed to hand over to you the second scroll. As I will not be here for next three months, it will give you enough time to grasp the essence of its message.'

'You could have called me.' Ajay was feeling a little ashamed that Vinay was taking so much trouble for him.

'So, what were you doing,' Vinay asked seeing Ajay's laptop open and that he was moving the cursor so that the laptop does not go into sleep mode.

'I was making my EMI payment for the home loan and other utility bills. I don't like dragging the payment to the last day.'

'Looks like I have come at the right time,' exclaimed Vinay.

'You finish your work and then I will give you the scroll.'

Ajay was little surprised and was wondering why Vinay told that he has come at the right time. Nevertheless, he went ahead to complete his transactions.

Once Ajay had shutdown his laptop, Vinay took out the letter from his pocket and handed it to him.

Dear Son,

A part of all you earn is yours to keep.

Lovingly yours,
Ram Prasad

Ajay looked at Vinay and then back to the letter. Seeing Vinay smiling, he knew that there must be some great wisdom in those few words. He read it again and then folded the paper and gave it back to Vinay.

'Isn't everything that I earn mine to keep?' questioned Ajay.

'Far from it,' replied Vinay. 'Now that you have made your customary payments for your home loan EMI, credit card and other utility bills, how much is left from your salary income that you received?'

Ajay recollected his account balance and realised what Vinay was trying to convey. 'Hardly 15% to 20% of my income,' he said meekly.

'Do you realise that even before your salary gets credited to your account, the Government takes away its share in the form of Income Tax? And once it comes to your account, what do you do with it? You pay the Credit Card Company, you pay for the bank loan, you pay for various utilities that you enjoy in the form of electricity, internet, mobile phone and then you pay for your basic necessities like food and clothing. And once all these payments are done, you indulge yourself in luxuries and at the end of the month you have hardly anything left for you.'

'So what is actually happening is that you pay everyone except you. To put it differently, *everyone is getting paid except the person who earned the pay cheque,*' continued Vinay. 'You work for everyone right from the government to the bank to the grocery store to the garment makers and at the end of the month you realise that you have nothing for yourself.'

'But shouldn't I be making payment to government and banks? Also, I need to make payment for my utility bills,' retorted Ajay.

'I am not saying that you default in your payments. What I am trying to say is that *you should pay yourself first[8] before you make any payment to others – that is – you should keep aside a portion of your income for yourself as soon as you get your salary.* This is the golden rule to become rich and I repeat for your own benefit: *Invest a portion of your income every month for long-term growth before you make any other payments.* This part of your salary and/or income shouldn't be less than one-tenth of your gross income no matter how little you earn. It can be as much as you can but it should not be less than one-tenth of your gross income. And on this part of your income no one but only you and your family should have a right, i.e. no other person or entity should lay its claim on this part of your income. Even the greatest investor of our time, Warren Buffet tells us: *"Don't save what is left after spending; spend what is left after saving."'*

---

[8]The 'Concept of Pay Yourself First' has been beautifully captured by George Samuel Clason in his book, *The Richest Man in Babylon* first published in 1926.

'I am already stretched. After making all the necessary expenses, I hardly have anything left. How will I manage in 90% of my income?'

'Well, do you know about Parkinson's Law?' said Vinay.

Ajay shrugged his shoulder indicating his ignorance on the subject.

'Parkinson's Law tells that *work expands so as to fill the time available for its completion.* In a nutshell; Parkinson's law means that if you give yourself a week to complete a two-hour task, then it will take the full week to complete that task even though it could conceivably be knocked out in the next two hours.'

'The same principle applies when it comes to money: *expenses always rise to match income.* That is why so many people never have enough money to save and invest, no matter how much their income increases or how old they become. With each raise they get, they end up spending more money. Let me give you some examples.' Vinay thought for some time and then continued, 'You have a car, you make more money by working hard and you get a better car. You have a house, you get a promotion and your salary increases and then you get a bigger house. You have clothes, you make more money and you get nicer clothes. You have holidays, you make more money and then you spend more money in holidays. So what is happening is that with every increase in your income, your expenses increase and you keep putting off your savings and investments, until unfortunately, it's too late. So until you discipline yourself, you will always end up with your expenses matching your income and at the end of the month you will have no savings.'

Ajay was now thinking about his salary when he had started his job. Presently, he was earning more than three times of what he was making when he had started his career but still he was not able to save much for himself and his family.

'If you look at your salary slip, you would notice that apart from the Income tax there is one more deduction in your salary,' said Vinay.

Ajay opened his laptop and went through his past two-three payslips and then said, 'I guess you are talking about Provident Fund deduction.'

'Yes, the Employee Provident Fund or Provident Fund (PF) as it is popularly known. While, income tax deducted from your salary goes to the Government, the PF deduction goes to a Government body called Employees' Provident Fund Organisation (EPFO) which maintains a fund in your name. Further, while the money deducted as income tax is not yours – that is you cannot use the money deducted as income tax for your own purpose, the money deducted as PF is entirely yours. Many people hate seeing PF deduction in their payslip but what they don't realise is that the Government is forcefully making you *pay yourself first.*"

'I didn't get what you are trying to say,' said Ajay who was a little curious now.

'First, you need to understand that the money deducted as PF from your salary is entirely yours and nobody else's. Only you have full right over it. Government understands the importance of *pay yourself first* strategy and it also understands that if you give entire salary to people, they will not be able to save for themselves. Hence, our Government has devised an automatic system wherein 12% of employees' Basic Salary and his Dearness Allowance is deducted and kept in his PF account and the balance amount is then credited to the individuals' salary accounts. And to help employees, the Government asks the employers – the company you are working for – to contribute a matching amount into employees PF account. This money maintained in your PF account is fully yours as it has been deducted from your salary.'

'I understand that by deducting a small amount from my salary even before I get to see it, the Government is helping me build a fund for myself. But what would be its value? It's only 12% of my basic salary, besides there is no DA for private company employees. How much would it have grown up to?' asked Ajay.

'How long have you been working?' asked Vinay.

'It's close to eight years.'

'I guess you wouldn't have withdrawn any money from your PF account.'

'No. I haven't withdrawn a single rupee from my PF account,' said Ajay.

'Then, why don't you login and check your PF balance?'

Ajay logged into his EPFO account and downloaded his passbook. When he opened the passbook his jaw dropped in surprise. 'What! I have seven and half lakh rupees in my PF account. I can't believe it.'

'Well, that's the power of *'pay yourself first.'* Instead of you deducting a portion of your salary at the beginning of the month and keeping it in some pension plan or retirement account for yourself, the government is doing this for you. And in just eight years, your small contribution has built up to seven and half lakh rupees. However there is one limitation with PF account – that is, you cannot access this PF account as easily as you can access your saving account funds. This PF amount is basically for your retirement but there are provisions in which you can withdraw it.'

'Now let me tell you something. Since people don't have easy access to their PF amount, they do not spend it. But, if they had easy access to PF amount then they would have spent that as well. *Most people if they get their hands on their PF amount would spend it.* Just because they are not able to see it; and in most of the cases are unaware of it, they leave it to grow with time. Remember, everyone is a victim of Parkinson's Law – your expense will always rise to match your disposable income.'

'So, just like everyone is able to manage in the income which they receive after income tax and PF deduction, everyone can also manage in 90% of their income that they receive post all deductions. Only thing is that they need to keep it aside even before they see it. And the simplest way to do this is to *give a Standing Instruction to you bank to deduct 10% of your salary at the start of every month and put it in Fixed Deposit, some Systematic Investment Plan or in your retirement account as per your choice.* So once that 10% of your salary is gone to some investment tool even before you saw it, you don't have control over it and you cannot spend it. After all, *you can't spend what you don't see.*'

'But, if the government is already forcing us to 'pay ourselves first' then why should we do it separately?' asked Ajay.

'The Government is doing that not to make you rich but to ensure that you don't have a tough time when you are retired. Also, it assumes that you would be working in a job throughout your working life. But, if you want to retire early, or start something of your own or if you want to become rich and wealthy, then the PF money will not be sufficient. You need to create your own fund and for that you need to do your own part by playing *"pay yourself first"* strategy.'

'But shouldn't we enjoy and make our life more comfortable with our increase in salary and income? After all, we work so that we can improve our standard of living and lead a comfortable life,' said Ajay.

'You should aim to improve your standard of living and lead a comfortable life. And that is why I insist on savings and investments. Most of the people think short term and spend everything on upscale consumer goods thinking that they are improving their lifestyle. But this so called improvement by buying bigger cars, houses, consumer goods and furniture is superficial and unsustainable. In reality, they downgrade their lifestyle by falling into debt trap and the vicious cycle of EMI. While to the outer world, they may project themselves to be progressing well in their life and career by showing off their newly acquired stuffs such as bigger cars, better furniture and other expensive household items which most of them have purchased on credit; internally they lead a life of fear, uncertainty and continuous stress of making loan payments on time. And with such stress, they are not able to actually enjoy their life.

'They think that since they have got hike and increment they should start spending like other rich people do. But they do not know the homework that rich people have done before they start to spend. Rich people know that if they need to build a tall skyscraper, they first need to dig a deep hole and create a strong foundation and then build the skyscraper. Other Rich people see that skyscraper, appreciate its beauty and think about the effort that would have gone in creating the foundation for the building which has made it stable because they too have done the same process and that is why they are rich.'

'But what does the Middle-class see? They only see the skyscraper which is above the ground. They don't see the foundation below the ground because they have never created such foundation for themselves. And when the luck favours them by way of salary hike on promotion or salary jump on job switch, they don't create the foundation. They start building their dream home; their own skyscraper without a proper foundation. And what happens when the building has been made. It falls down since it does not have any strong foundation to support it. So my friend, *I insist you to first build a strong foundation before you enjoy the benefits of your skyscraper. Otherwise, the view from the windows of your skyscraper would soon be lost.*'

Ajay thought for some time. He knew that Vinay was speaking truth. Without a strong foundation, you cannot have a tall building. He realised he too, tried to create his skyscraper without a proper foundation. This was the reason his skyscraper had fallen down even before it could be completed. He then asked, 'How do we then build a strong foundation?'

'Don't fall victim to Parkinson's Law. Start "Paying Yourself First." While you should improve your lifestyle with increase in your income, you need to break the Parkinson's Law to increase your savings and build wealth for yourself. And it can be done by following three simple steps,' Vinay then took out a piece of paper, scribed on it for some time and then handed the paper to Ajay.

1. Keep aside at least one-tenth of your gross income no matter how little you earn. Keep it in a safe investment tool and let it grow with time. You should refrain yourself from using this fund as much as possible.

2. For every hike in your salary or income, save and invest at least 50% of the increment for the rest of your career. And the balance amount of the increment can be utilised towards improving your standard of living.
3. Always count your expenses in absolute value and savings as a percentage of your income.[9]

After Ajay had finished reading, Vinay said: 'If you notice the point two, you would observe that by following this step, you are able to improve your lifestyle by enjoying and indulging in your desires but at the same time you are able to increase your savings and investments.'

Vinay let Ajay read all the three points again and then said, 'Do you know who plays the 'Pay Yourself First' strategy the best?'

'Don't know,' said Ajay.

'It's the Government,' said Vinay with a smile.

'Yeah, you just told how Government plays 'pay yourself first' on our behalf by deducting PF amount from our salary even before we get to see it and then depositing it in our name with EPFO.'

'That the Government does for the benefit of salaried employees. For its own benefit, the Government plays the 'Pay yourself first' strategy in the best possible way,' said Vinay.

Ajay looked at Vinay with surprise. His expression clearly told that he was curious to know how Government plays 'pay yourself first' strategy.

'If you see your payslip, you will notice that your Income

---

[9] This particular advice has been taken from the book *10 Commandments of Financial Freedom* by Mehrab Irani.

Tax has already been deducted even before it got credited to your account. Generally the tax on your income crystallises only on the completion of the last year. That is; first people earn their income for the year and based on the income earned by them during the previous year they need to pay tax accordingly. From the government's point of view, however there is a problem with this system. They know that people just couldn't be counted on to budget well enough to have their money in reserve to be able to pay their taxes the following year when it technically becomes due. So what did the Government do? They created a system to make sure that it got paid first, i.e. it started collecting tax as soon as you earned. Income tax is deducted from your pay cheque even before you get to see the full amount that you had earned.'

'The Government however has to justify this act. So, they have come up with the explanation that for ease of collection and regularity of flow of funds in to the Government for its various activities, it is collecting the taxes in advance during the year of earning itself. And they have named it as 'pay as you earn' concept. However, the real motive of collecting the tax in advance is that the Government knows the power of *Pay Yourself First* strategy and they are simply following it.'

Ajay was surprised to learn that the Government can be so smart. He never had understood that by deducting Income Tax every month from tax payers, the Government was leaving no stone unturned to get its money and that too before time. And this; the Government was able to do by simply *paying itself first.*

Vinay saw Ajay thinking. He waited for some time and then spoke: 'If you kept for yourself one-tenth of all you earnings, how much would you have in ten years?'

'I guess it would amount to as much as I earn in a year,' replied Ajay.

'You speak but half the truth, my friend,' said Vinay. 'Every rupee that you save and invest is a like an employee who works for you. Every rupee it earns is its child, which once invested also earns for you. So if you want to become wealthy then every rupee you save must earn and its children should also earn and its children's children should continue the process so that all may help to give you the abundance you have always desired.'

'Wealth like a tree, grows from a tiny seed,' continued Vinay. 'The first rupee that you save and invest is the seed from which your tree of wealth shall grow. The sooner you plant that seed the sooner the tree shall grow. And the more faithfully you nourish and water that tree with consistent savings and investments, the sooner you will enjoy in contentment beneath its shade.'

'So, if I keep saving a minimum of one-tenth of my earnings, it will help me become rich?' questioned Ajay.

'Just saving a portion of your earnings will not make you rich. You should understand that there is a fundamental difference between savings and investments. Savings does not grow with time. Our dear friend *inflation* reduces the value of savings every year. The amount of food that you can purchase from a hundred rupee note two years down the line will always be less than what you can get today. Inflation reduces the value of your money. So in order to become rich, you need to beat inflation and that can be done by proper investment where you get return which is higher than the inflation rate.'

'When you are just saving some portion of your earnings, you are simply creating a bench of employees who come to your office, mark their attendance, play around for the day and then leave at 5PM,' continued Vinay. 'These employees do not bring any money to you. To become rich, you have to make them productive and that can be done only when you put them to work. Investment does the exact thing for you. It let your money work for you. Investment let the money grow with time but savings reduces the value of money with time.'

Ajay was looking attentively towards Vinay. It was all making sense to him now. He was realising his mistakes and promised himself that he will follow this *Pay yourself first* strategy no matter what.

'Do you know the real beauty of *Pay Yourself First* strategy?' asked Vinay.

Ajay became eager knowing that there is something more to understand. He moved a little closer towards Vinay to listen what he has to say.

'To make money from your job, you go to your office and work hard for nine hours. In many instances you have to stretch yourself to meet certain deadlines or to listen and take care of some client request. In essence, it is you who is working hard to get that monthly salary. With *Pay Yourself First* strategy, it is not you, but your money which you have put in some proper investment tools, working for you. These monies are your employees who are constantly at work for you to fetch you a good return. They are at work making money for you when you are working in your office and they are at work when you are sleeping. All the rich people know this secret and that is why *they don't work for money, they let their money work for them*. Actually if you want to become truly rich and wealthy you have to create a big army of employees who are constantly at work, only then you can enjoy all the luxuries that you have always dreamed of.'

'Tell me seriously, is a saving of 10% of my income post deductions enough to make me rich or do I need to save and invest more?' asked Ajay.

'Well when you set aside 10% of your income definitely it will improve your position on the asset front. But if you want to know exactly how much you should save and invest before you start spending your income, here is the formula.[10] Remember, this formula is not dependent on your gross income but on the percentage of your income that you pay yourself first.'

Vinay then took out another sheet of paper from his pocket and handed it over to Ajay. It read as:

If you want to become...

Dead Broke (someone who might have to file for bankruptcy very soon): Don't pay yourself first. Spend more than you make. Borrow money on credit cards and carry debt you can't pay off.

Poor: Think about paying yourself first, but don't actually do it. Spend everything you earn every month and save nothing. Keep telling yourself, 'Someday I will begin paying myself first....'

Middle-class: Pay Yourself First 5% to 10% of your income.

Upper Middle-class: Pay Yourself First 10% to 15% of your income.

Rich: Pay Yourself First 15% to 20% of your income

---

[10]The formula has been proposed by David Bach in his book, *The Automatic Millionaire*.

Rich Enough to Retire Early: Pay Yourself First at least 20% of your income. There is no upper limit here.

Ajay's eyes gleamed as he was now able to see the picture of wealth and richness to which he had been blind till now. He could now picture himself with abundance of wealth and material. And he knew that the path to such success can only be achieved when he disciplines himself so that he is able to pay himself first as much as possible and invest that money into proper investment tool.

Ajay then looked at the paper which Vinay had given him and went through the three points again. He was convinced of the first two points but didn't understand the third point and asked Vinay to explain it.

'The third point just tells that you should not increase your expenses in proportion to the increase in your income. When you mentally account for your expenses in absolute terms, you will know when your expense is increasing. It will help you break Parkinson's Law.'

Meanwhile Priya had come out of the bathroom and was looking fresh in her *salwar* suit. She greeted Vinay with a smile and went and sat beside Ajay, who then explained to her about how *Pay Yourself First* strategy helps in increasing savings and this savings when properly invested ultimately led to creation of asset and wealth. He also explained to her about the Parkinson's Law and the three steps to break it so as to become rich and wealthy.

Suddenly Kiara got up from her sleep and Ajay immediately jumped from the sofa to fetch her. He came back running with Kiara sitting on his head and laughing heartily.

'Don't run so fast,' cautioned Priya.

Ajay then introduced Vinay to Kiara. 'Beta, he is Vinay Uncle,' said Ajay pointing Kiara's hand towards Vinay.

Vinay extended his hand towards her for a handshake but she took her hand back and hid her face behind her father's head.

'You both play with her. I will go and prepare our breakfast,' said Priya getting up from the sofa.

While Ajay was playing with her daughter, his mind was lingering with the learning that he got from Vinay today. He said to himself; 'Definitely, a part of all I earn is mine to keep!'

Seven

CREATE A GREAT OFFENCE AND A STRONG DEFENCE

Vinay reached the Bengaluru International Airport in the evening. He was flying to San Francisco from where he would take a connecting flight to San Diego – his company's headquarters. It was a three-month long trip as he had to work on a new platform whose prototype his team in the USA had developed. He was excited to meet some of his colleagues with whom he had interacted on mail and teleconference but never had a chance to meet in person.

After clearing the emigration check and completing the necessary formalities, he was waiting at the designated gate from where he would board his flight. He was observing the crowd and found that barring few foreigners it was mostly a group of Indians. While some of them appeared to be travelling with family, there were many who seemed to be travelling alone. He thought that just like him, all these fellows too would be working in one of the US technology companies and would be going to San Jose, San Diego or Santa Clara.

Soon the announcement was made for all the passengers travelling to San Francisco with the Singapore Airlines to assemble at Gate number eleven. Vinay like an obedient student stood in the queue that had already formed even before the announcement was completed. He was holding his laptop bag in his left hand and had his passport and boarding pass in his right hand. He waited patiently for his turn for verification of his boarding pass by the flight crew and then crossed the aerobridge to enter the flight. He was greeted by two air hostesses and after crossing the business class compartment, he went and sat in his seat.

Once he had made himself comfortable in his seat, Vinay pulled out his phone and called his wife Ananya to inform her that he has boarded the flight. Ananya enquired about the flight, fellow passengers and asked him to call her once he reached San Francisco. He sent his love and asked her to take care of the kids before switching off his mobile.

The flight took off on time. There was a screen behind every seat with a control panel and headphone for infotainment. Vinay switched on the screen in front of him and it displayed the route that the flight would take to reach San Francisco along with the total time of the journey. He then went to the movie section on the screen, browsed through the list of movies available but couldn't zero-in for a movie. He switched off the screen and took out *Kane and Abel* from his bag and started reading it.

After an hour of the journey, the flight crew started serving dinner to passengers. Vinay put down his book in the pouch in front of him and was waiting anxiously for the food as it had been more than 8 hours since he had his lunch.

'Vegetarian please,' Vinay told the air hostess as she served dinner.

Vinay watched carefully as the air hostess put the plate on the tray. He opened the packing and was delighted to find his favourite vegetable *biryani* as one of the items in his dinner plate. He enjoyed the meal – ate his favourite dish happily.

After the crew members took away the plates, Vinay took out a magazine from his bag. While browsing through the pages, he came across a news article which discussed about the upcoming football match between India and Oman. Oman at the world ranking of 101 was ranked 40 places higher than India in the pecking order and was clearly the favourites. Vinay went through the article which discussed how the present Indian Team under the new English Coach has performed better in the recent past and that it would not be a surprise if India beats Oman in the match.

While he was reading the article, he was reminded of Imran Rashid; his football coach during his NIT days at Allahabad. Rashid Sir as the students used to call him, was popular among all the football players in the institute. It was during his final year when Vinay was part of the Institute Football team and was to play for his college in the inter-NIT sports festival that he had formed a close bonding with him. Very soon he went off to sleep and started remembering the last few days of his college which he had spent with Rashid Sir.

It was a Friday evening and after having a rigorous practice for two hours Vinay was resting near one of the goal posts and relaxing his muscles. He was then joined by Rashid who told him about few of his faults during the practice session and also asked him to play from midfield for the next two practice matches. While they were relaxed and discussed trivial topics, Rashid asked him his thoughts about his new journey as a professional engineer. Vinay told him that he is excited about it as he would be moving to a bigger city – Bengaluru – the silicon valley of India. He also told him about the lessons that he had learnt from his father about money and laws of wealth creation and accumulation. Rashid then asked about the various lessons that Vinay has learnt in the past and was happy to understand about the importance of money that Vinay's father had told him.

'Since you are interested in money-making – already taking lessons from your father, I will tell you some of the principles of *wealth creation and protection* from my side which I have learned from my experience,' said Rashid.

'Yes; definitely. Please share your experience,' Vinay was excited to learn rules of *wealth creation and protection* from his football coach.

Rashid then picked a broken twig fallen from a nearby tree and drew a diagram on the ground.

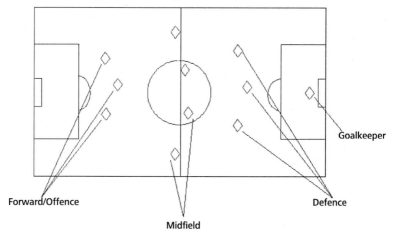

'Well, you already know the different roles each player has in the game,' said Rashid. 'The forward/offence tries to score goals for the team, the defence acts as a strong wall to the opposition attack, the midfield disrupts the opposing team's attacks as well as tries to create opportunities for their own team's forwards to convert goals and the goal keeper saves goals for his team.'

Vinay nodded silently looking at the diagram thinking what the football team has to do with rules of wealth protection.

'What happens when your team scores more goals than the other team?' asked Rashid.

'You win,' said Vinay.

'And what happens when your team scores fewer goals and concedes more goals to the other team?'

'You lose.'

'Correct. The same principle applies to our life when it comes to money.'

'How this principle works with the money?' Vinay was now curious to know what his coach was explaining to him.

'Scoring goals is like earning money. Just like the forward/attack players score goals for the team, the bread earners of the family earn money for the family. Conceding goals to the other team is like spending money. While few of your expenses are necessities and has to be met and sometimes you may indulge in some luxuries, your total spending determines total goals that you have conceded to your opponent.' Rashid paused for a moment to see if Vinay was understanding whatever he was explaining to him and then continued 'And just like in a game of football, if you score more goals than goals conceded then you win the match; *similarly in life if you earn more than what you spend then you win otherwise you lose.*'

'And what happens if my spending is same as my earning?' asked Vinay.

'The match ends in a draw. You do not move anywhere. You stand at the same place after the match where you were standing when it began. You spend 90 minutes running after the ball and in the end realise that you have gained nothing from the match.'

'Just like it's the difference between the goals scored and goals conceded which determines whether you have won the match or lost it,' continued Rashid 'similarly it's the difference between your earnings and your total spending which determines whether you are making any progress in your life.'

'I understand your point,' Vinay told after thinking for some time. 'Similar to the game of football, in life also *you need to have a great offence and a strong defence to create and protect your money respectively.*'

'Exactly!' spoke Rashid.

'But how do we build a great offence and strong defence for ourselves in real life?' asked Vinay.

'To build a great offence you need to develop some skills and then use those skills through labour to earn money. And to create a strong defence you should learn to differentiate between necessities and unnecessary expenses and try to control your unnecessary expenses. *This part of the game – the defence – is the foundation stone of wealth accumulation and you should labour hard to master this part.*'

'Can you please elaborate a little?' asked Vinay.

'Definitely; I would love to explain this to you. But it's getting late. Can you come to *Chowk* tomorrow evening and then we will discuss?'

'Sure Sir,' said Vinay with a smile.

Both the teacher and the student got up and started moving to their respective abode. The street lights were flooding the campus main road and very few students could be seen walking through the campus. While Vinay was going to his hostel to have his dinner at the hostel mess, Rashid moved towards his Maruti Swift parked under the tree behind the football ground to get back to his home at chowk. The campus was silent now except for some music coming from nearby hostels where students were playing *Metallica* at the maximum volume of their *Creative 2.1.*

Building a Great Offence

Find a Job that You Love

The next evening Vinay met Rashid at a roadside eatery near the Chowk. Both of them then had warm milk with some extra cream in earthen pot and then had a *gulab jamun* each. Rashid paid the bill and then they started moving towards Triveni Sangam. Once they had left the shop, Rashid asked Vinay what the eatery's owner does to make a living.

'He uses his skills of making sweets, confectionaries and *namkeens* and then sells them in the market.'

'Correct and what does that tailor do?' Rashid pointed to a nearby tailor who was busy in his sewing machine.

'He uses his tailoring skill by way of stitching and sewing dresses for people.'

'What about him?' Rashid was pointing to a board hanging outside a building which read 'Dr Prashant Mehra, MBBS, MD.'

'He is a medical practitioner and knows about various medicines and uses his knowledge to diagnose illnesses and prescribe medications to restore good health of the people.'

'See, in all these cases people uses their skills and knowledge to earn money for them. Their offence, i.e. their way of making money is to use their skills in which they are good at and then sell them in the market. *Everybody has some skills or talents and the person who utilises his talent to the maximum will create a great offence for himself. He will make a lot more money than the person who doesn't utilise his talent properly,*' spoke Rashid.

'But how can a tailor earn more than a doctor, even if he utilises his talent to his best' asked Vinay.

Rashid thought for some time and then spoke: 'Our society rewards people in different ways. Usually it follows a particular pattern and this is the reason why different people earn differently. It rewards those skills/talents

✓ which are scarce in society – which is in greater demand.
✓ whose acquisition takes hard work and time, i.e. acquiring that skill requires long effort such as architects, social scientists and chartered accountants, researchers, doctors, and engineers.
✓ lastly and most importantly people are paid in direct proportion to the value they deliver according to the market place.

It is because of these reasons that in most cases a doctor earns more than a tailor.'

'So you mean to say that in order to have a great offence, we need to develop those skills and talents, which are scarce as also take much time to master,' said Vinay.

'Suppose I tell you that a lawyer earns much more money than the average people in India. With this background in mind, you work hard to complete your LLB and then LLM and start your law practice. But then you realise that you do not really enjoy going to court and fighting cases for your clients. What would you do then?' asked Rashid.

'Probably I will quit my job and then do something which I would enjoy.'

'Then why not choose that profession you think you would enjoy and develop the skills and talents you would require to practice that profession at the first instance itself.' Rashid paused for a while and then continued, 'You should choose a profession, which appeals to you. One you think you can master and then excel in your profession. Once you excel in your profession then it doesn't matter which profession you have chosen, you would build a great offence for yourselves. Most of the rich people are those who enjoy their profession because having fun in the work motivates them to excel in their field. *You cannot become rich if you do not enjoy what you are doing.*'

'There is one simple question I ask to people who come to me seeking advice on how to become rich. I ask them 'If you won a cheque of ₹5 crores tomorrow, would you continue to do what you are currently doing?' While I am not sure what answers poor and middle-class would give to this question, rich and successful people will always say that they would continue doing what they are doing. However, they would only do it differently or better or at a higher level. But they love their work so much that they wouldn't even think of leaving it or retiring.'

Vinay nodded in agreement. But from his face, it was clear that he was not yet convinced. Rashid said if he had any doubt, then it's better to clarify.

'But how would a bus driver earn more than an engineer or a university professor even if he really loves his job?' asked Vinay.

'How much do you think Michael Schumacher or for that instance our own Narain Karthikeyan earn every year?' asked Rashid with a smile.

'I guess they earn in crores,' said Vinay.

'They earn more than we can imagine. If you ask what their profession is; then the answer is they drive, that is they are racing drivers. But they are best in their field. We can even take the example of Jawed Habib. What does he do? He is a hair expert or to put it simply he is a barber. Yet he earns more than any doctor, engineer or management gradate. Why is it so? It is because he chose the profession which appealed to him and then excelled in his field.'

'Another pertinent example you can think of is Sanjeev Kapoor. What is his profession? He is a chef. In other words, he is a trained cook. Now you may ask how a cook can earn more than doctors, engineers and professors. But in reality he earns more than most of the doctors, engineers and professors. Again, he took the profession which he liked, learned its intricacies, became the expert in his chosen domain and then suddenly he has become a celebrity. Now he comes in TV and other realty shows and makes millions. I can give you numerous examples where people have chosen the so-called low paying job but are making lots of money. It doesn't matter much which profession you are in. By developing more interest in your work, more concentration upon your job and with more persistence in your effort, you can increase your earning capacity. Always remember that *a man who seeks to learn more of his craft is always highly rewarded.*'

Rashid looked at Vinay who was listening to him attentively and then said *'It is not the profession but your love and dedication towards your profession which will help you rise up in your life.* If you want to become an engineer then become the best in your domain, if you want to become an accountant then become the best accountant and if you want to do your own business then become the best businessman in your field. *Anybody who is best in his chosen profession earns the most.*'

Take for example the case of professional sportsperson. It is usually the best players in every sport who earn the most. They also make the most money on endorsements. Hence, it should come as no wonder why Sachin Tendulkar and Dhoni are the richest cricketers in our present team. So if you want to earn more, then you should try to become the best in your chosen profession. And this can be done by learning the intricacies of your work and executing them in the best possible way.'

'But isn't learning the intricacies of the work, excelling in it and executing them in the best possible way difficult? After all everybody pursues a set of profession but not everybody become expert in that profession,' asked Vinay.

'Let me tell you a story that I read in the book, *You Can Win* by Shiv Khera,' spoke Rashid. 'Once there were three men laying bricks to build three different houses in a street. A man who was passing through the street asked each of them the same question, i.e. what were they doing? The first man said: "Don't you see that I am making a living for myself?" The second one said: "Don't you see I am laying bricks?" The third one replied: "I am building a beautiful house." Here, to an outsider it would seem that all three men are doing the same thing; but internally in their mind and heart, all the three were doing three different things. All the three had totally different perspectives on what they were doing. They had three different attitudes about their work. And will their attitude affect their performance? Yes. Would the three houses once built be same? Certainly not!'

'If you observe the three men laying bricks, you would notice that the first two lacked certain feeling which the third possessed in abundance. It is called *Pride in Performance*. Pride in performance does not represent ego. It represents pleasure with humility. It represents enjoying your work and executing it in the best possible way. Remember; *quality of the work and the quality of the worker are inseparable.* Anybody would tell about the greatness of the painter by merely seeing his paintings.'

'Now coming to your question on how do we bring excellence in our work? *Excellence comes when the performer takes pride in doing his best.* Every job is a self-portrait of the person who does it, regardless of what the job is, whether washing cars, sweeping the floor or painting a house.'

'It is sad that we as a society differentiate people based on their profession and think that a carpenter or a craftsman is smaller than a doctor or an engineer,' continued Rashid. 'In my opinion no profession is small and every profession provides an opportunity for anyone to rise to greatness. I would consider a carpenter who takes pride in his work, does his job in his best way by innovating new designs and coming up with new ideas in high regard than a doctor who doesn't do his job properly.'

'Martin Luther King Jr had once said: *If a man is called to be street sweeper, he should sweep streets even as Michelangelo painted, or Beethoven composed music, or Shakespeare wrote poetry. He should sweep streets so well that all the hosts of heaven and earth will pause to say, here lived a great street sweeper who did his job well.* The feeling of a job well done is a reward in itself.

And the more money that comes with a job well done is like icing on the cake.'

Vinay was looking more peaceful now for his curiosity was answered. He was smiling as he had grasped one of the key fundamental principles which would help him grow in his life.

'So to build a great offence one should choose a profession which appeals to him and in which he thinks he can enjoy himself and then excel in his profession by taking pride in his work and executing the work in the best possible way,' said Vinay.

'Correct! Now let me give you some statistics which will help you appreciate the fact that – the more people love their jobs, the quicker they get rich,' said Rashid. 'There was a survey done by one of the 'Big4' accounting firms where 80% people surveyed said they did not like their jobs. And in another survey conducted by Gallup, 63% of 2,30,000 employees in the survey said they were unhappy with their jobs.[11] The data of the survey was then analysed by Thomas Corley and he came out with some interesting findings.'

'And what were those findings?' Vinay was getting curious to know.

'The findings were that around *96% of the poor* did not like what they did for a living. Further, *86% of the rich* liked what they did for a living and *7% of the rich loved* what they did for a living. Indeed, the best part of the finding was that those 7% of the rich who loved their job had accumulated more than double the wealth of the rich people who liked their jobs.'

---

[11]These surveys were done in the year 2012 and 2013 respectively and do not necessarily align with the time frame of the story but nevertheless have been use to drive home the author's point of why loving one's job is important to get rich.

'Only when you love your job you would be passionate about it and only when you are passionate about your job, you will excel in it. And that is the reason why people who love their job are much wealthier than those who don't love their job.'

'So, it all boils down to this simple flow of facts:

1. When you love what you do for a living, you'll spend more time doing it.
2. When you spend more time doing what you love to do for a living, you'll get better at doing it.
3. When you are better at what you do than your competitors, the world will pay you more money.
4. When you make more money than your competitors, you can accumulate more wealth in a shorter period of time.

So, the essence of this survey and finding is that you need to love your job to get rich,' said Rashid.

'I see your point,' said Vinay. 'If I want to become rich, I need to find a job that I would love and never quit.'

'Correct!' exclaimed Rashid.

Learn to Adapt; Become a Continuous Learner

'But remember one thing. In whatever field you choose to work, always keep yourself updated with the latest trend that is happening in your field. It is because the work/process that you would be doing/following at one point of time would be completely replaced with a new set of work/process which would be more efficient than the last work/process and to execute that work you would need new set of skills. So, unless you keep learning new skills and you keep yourself updated with the latest trend in your profession you will fall behind. *Remember, as technology keeps accelerating the pace of change, no one can simply hold on to a job and expect that job to remain the same for ten or twenty years.'*

'Let me give you an example. There was a guy called Baldev, a woodcutter who worked in a timber mill for five years but never got any hike in his salary. The mill owner then hired another woodcutter called Govind and within a year he got raise. Baldev resented Govind getting the raise and that too in one year while he has been working hard and never got the hike in five years. He went to the mill owner and expressed his feelings. The mill owner said, 'You are still cutting the same number of trees you were cutting five years ago. We believe in results and would be happy to give you a raise if your productivity goes up.' Baldev then went back, started hitting harder and putting in longer hours but he still was not able to cut more trees. He went back to the mill owner and told his dilemma. The mill owner then told Baldev to go and talk to Govind. 'May be there is something Govind knows that you and I don't.' Baldev then approached Govind and asked how he managed to cut more trees. To which Govind replied, 'After every tree I cut, I take a break for two minutes and sharpen my axe. When was the last time you sharpened your axe?'

'Remember even in the present world, we need to keep on sharpening our axe at a regular interval. Past glory and impressive degrees don't count much when you are in the industry. What matters is – do you learn continuously, do you change your working style as per the need of the industry, do you keep yourself abreast with the latest development in your chosen profession and do you sharpen your axe regularly?'

'The *Survival of the Fittest* theory is just not a thing of the past. It was in work yesterday, it is in work today and it will be working tomorrow. Leon C Megginson, Professor of Management and Marketing at Louisiana State University have described it beautifully when he said: '*It is not the strongest or the most intelligent who will survive but those who can best manage change.*' There is a very beautiful book named. *Who Moved My Cheese* by Dr Spencer Johnson on the subject of change and adaptability to the new environment. I would like you to read it, so that you never fall behind others just because you are clinging to your old thoughts and habits.'

'Yes, I understand that. I have also read many articles which talk about reinventing oneself to stay updated because in the present world *change* is happening very fast. And if one is not able to align himself with the *change,* then he may fall behind others,' said Vinay.

'Correct! Many a times, people with some industry experience would complain that 'I have got ten years of experience. I don't know why I'm not getting paid better.' What they don't realise is that they don't have ten years of experience. What they have is one year's experience repeated ten times. They haven't made a single improvement, a single learning, a single innovation in nine years. And that is the reason they don't get paid any better. Remember, market always pays according to the value he/she delivers. It doesn't see the age and experience but the value that one would provide.'

Vinay now understood what Rashid Sir was trying to convey. He realised that in order to remain fit and to excel in one's profession, everyone has to keep on learning and improving on continuous basis.

'Now coming to the third point which is the most important factor in determination of one's income; that is you will be paid in direct proportion to the value you deliver according to market place. The key word is value. This value again depends on the number of people you provide your service to. Suppose there is a doctor who treats say 10–15 patients in a day and there is another doctor who has similar qualification but treats around 50–60 patients in a day. Who do you think would be earning more?'

'The second doctor'; came the prompt reply from Vinay.

'Do you know why Shah Rukh Khan earns more than any actor in India?'

'It's because he is one of the best actors in the industry.'

'No doubt he is a good actor, but there are better actors than him and not everyone gets paid that much. The reason Shah Rukh Khan earns much more than most of the actors lies in the size of the audience he entertains. He has a bigger fan following than most of the actors and he knows the fact that to earn more he needs to reach a much wider audience rather than produce the best films.'

'Take another example of a standalone grocery store and a chain of grocery stores. All the grocery stores provide almost the same quality of goods to their customers but the chain of stores serve more customers than a standalone store and hence earn much more. You have to think big and play big to earn more and create a strong offence. Most of the people rather choose to play small. Why? First reason is fear. They are scared to death of failure. Second, people play small because they feel small. They feel unworthy. They don't feel they're good enough or important enough to make a real difference in people's lives.'

'The problem with playing small is that people are not utilising their potential to the maximum. And when you are not using your potential fully, then you start living a mediocre life. And that is definitely not a good way to live. To live a fruitful life, use your potential to the fullest, think big, reach out to as many people as possible, try to serve/influence a bigger set of customers/audience and then your stream of cash inflows will increase.'

'So whatever game I am playing, I need to play it big. I need to think big and reach out to wider base of people rather than play small,' said Vinay.

'Right! But there is one more thing which can further enhance your offence.'

'And what is that?' asked Vinay. He was happy to learn the lessons of life and money that his coach was teaching him.

Create Multiple Sources of Income

'Every one of us has some gifted talent or potential apart from the talent and expertise which we use in our chosen profession. In most of the cases people are not aware of or even in case they know that they have some particular set of talent, they do not monetise them. That is, they do not make money from that talent because either they keep themselves busy in their work or believe that they do not have enough time to use their talent.'

'Do you know what my main profession is?' asked Rashid.

'You are a football coach, right,' said Vinay with a surprise.

'I am a businessman,' Rashid said with a smile. 'I have

two businesses. The first one is trading of readymade garments and the second one is of selling sports goods. I have both my shops in Chowk.'

'But, how come you are a football coach?'

'It is because; I decided to use my talent other than the one which I use in my business.'

Rashid then told him that he is a BCom graduate and that he has been in the business since he came out of his college. He also told him that he always loved playing football and even had played football at the State level. However, he could not make it to the National Team.

'So, when this notice came that NIT Allahabad was looking for a football coach, I immediately applied for it. Knowing that I as a football coach would report to the college only in evening time for most of the days and that my presence would be required full time only during Sports festival season or during inter-college competition, I was confident that taking up this job would not interfere with my main profession.'

'But not everybody play football at the State level,' said Vinay.

'Do you know about hummingbird?' asked Rashid.

'Yes, it is the smallest bird in the world.'

'And what is its specialty? What is its talent?'

Vinay thought for some time and then said, 'I am not able to recall.'

'Hummingbird, being the smallest of the birds weighs only about 2.5 to 5 grams. But it is their lightness which gives them the flexibility to perform complicated manoeuvres, such as beating its wings 75 times a second. This enables the hummingbird to fly at speeds exceeding 50km/hr backwards and to drink nectar from flowers while hovering, but it cannot soar, glide or hop like an eagle does. The Ostrich on the other hand is the largest of the birds weighing 70 to 120kg. Though it is the tallest and the largest of the birds, it cannot fly. However, its legs are so strong that it can run at up to 70km/hr, taking strides of 12–15 feet.'

Vinay was thoughtful and was trying to grasp what Rashid was trying to explain to him.

'See, what I am trying to say is that everyone has some talent or the other which one can use to make a second or multiple source of earning. It may be something different from your present profession or it may be related to your chosen profession. Say, you become an electronics engineer or software engineer. Then you can teach at a local college during weekends or you can provide training to fresh college graduates or you can work part time on some project as a freelancer.'

'All I am saying is that everybody on this earth is born with natural talents, things they are naturally good at. Somebody can be good in dance, some in singing, some has natural talent to play guitar well, some can play football or cricket well, or somebody can teach and speak well in public or somebody can be good in writing prose and poems. These talents or gifts given by God to us have been given for a specific reason: to use and share with others. *Research has shown that happiest people are those who use their natural talents to the utmost.* Part of your mission in life then must be to identify your natural talent and then to share your talent, your gift with as many people as possible. So when you are using your natural talent, it's a double advantage: first you enjoy what you are doing, you are getting the opportunity to pursue your hobby; second you generate an additional source of income for yourself.'

Rashid then stopped near a magazine shop and picked up a magazine with the cover page of Mr Mukesh Ambani with a subtitle at the bottom which read '*Reliance to venture into retail: New entity called Reliance Retail.*'

'Even the richest man of India is creating additional source of income,' said Rashid handing over the magazine to Vinay. 'Now you may ask why he needs to go into retail. After all he has established business in Oil and Gas and Petrochemicals. The answer is; it is because of creating multiple sources of income for him that he has become rich. *Rich people don't live on single source of income. They create multiple sources of incomes using their talent and a deep desire to create wealth for themselves and their family*'

Vinay then purchased the magazine and both of them continued their walk towards Triveni Sangam.

After Vinay had browsed through the magazine, Rashid spoke, 'There are vast opportunities available for all of us to make money. We just need to keep our mind open and be eager to create wealth for ourselves. *It is all about augmenting your primary source of income by using your skills and talents and then you will build a great offence for yourself.*'

Both of them had now reached the Triveni Sangam. The sight of Yamuna merging with the mighty Ganga was breathtaking. The legend says that at the point of confluence, it is not two but three rivers, the third being the invisible or mythical Saraswati River which merges with the other two viz. Ganga and Yamuna and that is why it is called Triveni.

Vinay went down the stairs to reach to the water and saw how Yamuna, which is deep but calm and greenish in colour, is merging with the Ganga which is shallow but forceful and clear at the confluence point. Rashid followed him and saw how Vinay was mesmerised seeing the vastness of the rivers. Both then went to a platform and sat there observing people offering evening *aarti* to the rivers. Many people were also taking a dip in the holy water at the point of confluence of Ganga and Yamuna to wash away all their sins and to free themselves from the cycle of rebirth.

Create a Strong Defence!

Rashid had asked Vinay to meet him the next day at his garment shop. Vinay parked his bicycle outside Rashid's shop, locked it and then went inside. He saw Rashid was busy selling readymade garments to his customer. Rashid noticed Vinay entering the shop and pointed him towards a seat and asked him to wait for some time. Vinay took his seat and was offered a cup of tea from one of Rashid's staff, which he politely accepted and started observing the actions, negotiations and settlement between Rashid/his staff and his customers.

Vinay noticed that after one of the customers had finalised a full sleeve shirt for himself, Rashid was persuading him to purchase a new pair of Jeans.

Rashid: Sir, you have a good taste. This shirt is the latest one in the market and we had got this shipped only last week from Kolkata.

Customer: Yeah, Thanks. But it's slightly costly.

Rashid: Sir, check the quality of the dress. It's far better than others, plus it's a branded one. It will suit your personality.

The customer checks the side of the shirt which he has finalised with his fingers and then compares it with his existing shirt and after convincing himself that he is going to purchase a better shirt, he asks Rashid to pack the shirt and prepare the bill.

Rashid: Sir, now that you have got yourself a nice shirt why don't you purchase a new pair of jeans. We have got fresh stock of material.

Customer: No, no. I already have three pairs of jeans. I don't require new one.

Rashid: Sir, but those are old ones and their colour has also faded (Rashid was pointing to the pair of jeans worn by the gentleman). And it will not match with your new shirt. Why don't you try a new pair of jeans?

Now the customer hesitated for a while yet asked Rashid to show him some pieces. He also warned that he may not purchase the jeans if he doesn't like them.

Rashid: Sir, you do not worry about that. You have a look at our new collection of jeans. I bet you will definitely find a pair of jeans from our fresh stock, which will match with your new shirt.

Vinay noticed how Rashid enthusiastically showed different pairs of jeans to the customer and in the end he saw the customer paying the bill for both a shirt and a pair of jeans.

Rashid then got up from his seat and asked Vinay to accompany him. Both of them then went to a nearby eatery shop where they had a plate of *samosa chaat* each. After having the evening snacks, both of them then started walking towards *Company Gardens.*

Know where your money goes; instead of wondering where it went

'Sir, last night I thought deeply about the ways that we discussed yesterday for building a great offence for ourselves and everything made sense to me. Now I am all the more eager to know about creating a strong defence so that we may protect our hard earned money and proposer and enjoy in wealth that we would create,' spoke Vinay.

'The first step to build a strong defence is through budgeting and planning and understanding the difference between your casual wishes and your long cherished desires,' said Rashid.

'I didn't understand it fully.'

'You would have observed many people who despite earning a good income for their family struggle financially at the end of the month. It is mainly because they do not know where and how they spend their money. And when they need some money for certain essential requirement, they are taken for surprise because they don't have the requisite amount of money in their account.'

'And since they need to meet their essential requirement, they resort to credit card and thus fall into debt trap. They don't realise where they are making mistakes and how their hard earned money is draining out from their wallet. Creating a budget help people realise where their money is going and also let them know where they can cut their expenses so that they can have surplus at the end of the month which they can put into proper investment tools to let their money grow with time.'

Rashid paused a little and then asked Vinay if he knows what is budgeting.

'Don't know much about it but have heard people telling that if you are living on a budget then you need to be frugal, that you should not go out to restaurants and movies and that you should not spend unnecessarily on any luxury items,' said Vinay.

'Looks like you have got it all wrong. What you told about budgeting is what most people understand and feel about budgeting and that is why they struggle. After all who wants to live a plain and boring life where there is no fun, no ice-creams, no movies and no outings and that is the reason they discard the concept of budgeting. You need to have fun in life where you can indulge yourself in some luxuries, where you go to nice hotels and restaurants and get good massage at some nice parlours and saloons.'

'Let me tell you what exactly a budget is and how it can help you create a strong defence,' said Rashid. 'John Maxwell; who is a famous American author and speaker has the best quote on budgeting. He says '*A budget is people telling their money where to go instead of wondering where it went.*' You have to make your money behave and this can be done by becoming the master of your money and telling them where to go by creating a budget and following it religiously. If you are spending your money on some necessary items, then you should know about it. Similarly, if you indulge yourself in some luxury, you should know how much money you spent on it.'

'*Most of the* Rich *people are masters of their money. They control their money through a careful budget. They know exactly where their money is going. Most of the middle-class and poorer people are slaves of the money. They wonder where their money went. They think that they know how they spent their money but in reality they do not have a clear idea about it. Also when they create a budget, people decrease their stress level because with a positive plan of expenses, there are no surprises.'*

'I understand that with budgeting I would get to know where my money has to go. Will it help me increase my savings?'

'When you create a budget for yourself, you will allocate a certain portion of your income towards long term investments, a portion towards meeting your monthly expenses, a portion towards recreation and indulgence in luxury goods. Of course you will also need a buffer to meet unseen expenses. When you list down your monthly expenses, you will realise that you have been wasting your money on some undue items which you can very easily curb. This will help you increase your savings.'

'I got your point. But how should we define our budget, i.e. how much should we allocate to various heads?' asked Vinay.

'That is a very good point,' said Rashid with a smile. 'Very often people allow their income to define their budgets – that is they will allocate their monthly expenses which they also call as necessary expenses according to their income. They don't realise that *what each of us call our necessary expenses will always grow to equal our income unless we protest to the contrary.* In order to become rich, one should allocate not more than 80% of their income towards monthly expenses and recreational activities, 10% towards unseen expenses which they should put in short term investments and a minimum of 10% towards long term investments.'

'Shouldn't we rather enjoy with our money. I believe it is everyone's right to enjoy the good things of life which they can through the use of money. If people start living with lesser amount of money than they earn then aren't they forgoing the pleasure that the life has to offer to them?'

'We should learn to differentiate between necessary expenses and desires. All of us have multiple desires which cannot be gratified with our income. Hence even if you spend all your income then you will be able to gratify only a portion of your desires and will be left with many ungratified desires.'

'The renowned author *George Clason* has rightly said that 'just as weeds grow in a field wherever the farmer leaves space for their roots, even so freely do desires grow in men whenever there is possibility of their being gratified. The purpose of a budget is to have your necessities and in so far as attainable your other desires realised. *The budget enables you to realise your most cherished desires by defending them from your casual wishes.* Like a bright light filtering into a dark cave, your budget shows up leaks from your wallet and enables you to stop them and control your expenditures which then can be used for definite and gratifying purposes."

Vinay was now realising the importance of budget. He now knew that to have a strong defence one should do proper budgeting.

Automate the System

'But, people tell it's very hard to follow the budget and it requires a lot of discipline. They tell that you need to list down each and every expense of yours and since it is very painful and time consuming they ultimately don't follow it,' said Vinay.

'There is an easy way to follow the budget and you don't need to be too much disciplined to save your income.

Whenever you get your monthly salary, deduct 10% of it and put it in a Fixed Deposit. This will take care of your short term investments which can be used to meet certain unseen expenses. And then put 10% in some long term investment tools such as Public Provident Fund, Stocks and Mutual Funds which you should not try to liquidate unless your house is on fire. And now you have 80% of your income which you can allocate among your necessary and luxury expenses. You can do all this by automating the system of deduction by telling your Bank to put 10% of your money in FD/RD and 10% of your money in some long term investment tools of your choice as and when you get your salary. And since banks are disciplined in their assigned task, you do not need to worry about being disciplined. Also, once the decision is out of your hands over 20% of your income, there's no way you can be tempted into doing something wrong. It's called '*protecting you from yourself* strategy.'

Rashid paused for some time to let Vinay realise how easy it is to create and follow budget where you don't have to think anything about it – your bank does the job for you. He then continued, 'Just tell your bank to make the automatic deduction at the beginning of every month and you don't need to do anything. It's as simple as that.'

Want to Be Rich? Study the Rich Live-Style

'If you go to a low budget gym where there is nobody to guide you or if you sign up for a costly gym with latest equipment and doesn't opt for personal trainer then how would you practice your workout?' asked Rashid.

'By observing the lean and muscular people working out in the gym,' replied Vinay.

'Correct. Similarly, *if you want to be rich, you should study the habits and value systems of the rich.* Rich people believe that financial independence is more important than displaying high social status and always live below their means. They take out time to create budget for themselves and stick to it. '

'But why does Rich people need to budget. After all they have all the money to gratify their desires?' asked Vinay.

'They have become rich by a budget. A control of their expenses helps maintain their affluent status the same way,' said Rashid. 'When you go to the gym, you will see many people who are physically fit, have a lean and muscular body. You would say that they don't need to go to the gym. Yet it is because they go to gym regularly that they are fit. Similarly, it *is because rich people follow their budget regularly that they are rich.*'

'Everybody desires to have a fit body and they also know what is required to achieve that. But despite this, not everybody is physically fit. It is because they don't have the discipline and desire to do it. Similarly, everyone wants to become rich and wealthy and they also know that to become rich and wealthy one has to increase his income, cut down his expenditure and invest his savings in proper investment tools. But not everyone becomes rich. Why? It is because they are not disciplined to control their expenses. They don't take out time to budget or plan. Rich people are much more disciplined when it comes to money unlike the middle-class and poor people. *It's ironic that the many men and women who work hard day in and day out at jobs they don't necessarily like, when asked to take time to design their own futures; to create budget, often reply: I don't have the time for that as I am too busy in my life.'*

'So if I want to become rich, I also need to create financial plan for myself to work according to it.'

'Yes! You just need to create a financial plan for yourself and then automate the system. Believe me it is very easy. *You just need to tell your plan to your bank once – then forget it.* While you enjoy and indulge yourself with various luxuries and funs, your bank will take care of your investments. You don't need to be disciplined. Your bank takes care of the discipline part,' Rashid said with a smile.

A Rupee Saved Is Not a Rupee Earned

While they were walking, Rashid spoke, 'You would have heard people telling that a rupee saved is rupee earned.'

'Yes, people often tell that to encourage savings. They say that if I am able to save a rupee then it is as good as earning a rupee.'

'While people say that in good intention, what they say is entirely wrong,' said Rashid.

'You mean to say that a rupee saved is not rupee earned?' asked Vinay who was a little surprised now.

'Yes, it is entirely wrong. In fact the truth is that *a rupee saved is one and half times a rupee earned.*'

'How?' asked Vinay.

'Income Tax,' said Rashid with a smile.

'I didn't get it,' spoke Vinay.

Suppose, you are in the highest tax bracket which I am very sure you will be once you start earning. Assume, you earn ₹150.

But you don't get the entire ₹150 that you earned. You will receive only ₹105 and the balance ₹45 will go as income tax to the government. Remember, there is a difference between your earnings and the amount that you get in your savings account; the difference being the income tax which the government legally takes away from you.'

'For your understanding, consider your net income post income tax to be ₹100, instead of ₹105 and gross income to be ₹150. Now, listen carefully to what happens in real life. You earn ₹150 but you get ₹100. Now if you spend the entire ₹100 then you have spent your entire earning of ₹150.'

'How?' asked Vinay.

'It is because to spend ₹100, you need to earn ₹150. So, if you are not spending ₹100 then in reality you are actually earning ₹150 and not ₹100. And that is why, I say *a rupee saved is one and half times a rupee earned.*'

Vinay was in shock upon this revelation. He never had realised that his *saving was one and half times more powerful than his earning.*

'Always remember, *to spend ₹100 you need to earn ₹150.* Rich people understand this fundamental and that is why they stress more on savings rather than on increase in their earnings. They know that *it is much easier to save ₹100 than to put an effort to earn extra ₹150.* When you save, the entire money is yours. But when you try to earn extra, the entire income is not yours. The government takes tax from your extra income and you get only 70% of your earned money. So whenever you go out to spend money on your desires, always keep in mind if your desire of ₹100 is really worth of your extra effort that you would put to earn ₹150. Only if you think it is worth it then go ahead and spend. Otherwise, it is always better to save that ₹100 because that way you are saving yourself from putting an extra effort to earn ₹150.'

Vinay was completely in awe of his football coach. He realised it was such a simple thing and yet it is missed by most of the people. He then thought that probably that may be the reason not all people are rich in the world.

Don't fall prey to Diderot Effect!

Both of them had reached the Company Gardens by now. It was now dusk, there were few people walking in the garden. Vinay also saw some people jogging in the garden. All these people were fit and it seemed that they do not need to jog, after all they are fit. Yet he remembered the words of Rashid to realise it is because they jog regularly that they are fit.

Rashid then purchased two cones of peanuts from the nearby stall and then they went to a wooden bench for some rest. While munching on the peanuts, Rashid asked Vinay if he knows about Denis Diderot, the French philosopher of 18th century. Vinay replied he has never heard of him.

'In the eighteenth century, the French philosopher Denis Diderot wrote an essay entitled *Regrets on Parting with My Old Dressing Gown,'* said Rashid.

'And what was that essay about?' asked Vinay.

'The essay talked about how possession of a new thing which does not conform with your existing possessions forces you into a series of new purchases to upgrade your old stuff, resulting into over consumption and ultimately into debt trap,' said Rashid.

'I didn't get it completely.'

'Well, it goes something like this. In the 18th century, Denis Diderot received a gift: a beautiful scarlet dressing gown from someone. The fabric of the gown was gorgeous and its colours were rich and vibrant. The craftsmanship of the gown was spectacular too. On receiving such a wonderful gown, Diderot immediately threw his tattered old gown away. He didn't need it anymore. His new gown was breath-taking. Even then, he needed to make a few extra purchases to accommodate that gown.

'In the past, if one of his books was covered with dust, he'd simply use his old gown as a rag to remove the dust from the book. Now he couldn't wipe away dust with his beautiful new gown. He'd need to buy some dust rags. Also, when there was excess ink on his pen, he used his old gown to wipe it clear. But he couldn't do that with the new gown. It would ruin his newly acquired gown. So, he would now need to buy handkerchiefs, or perhaps he'd need better pens.'

'But those were small purchases and Diderot thought that these are small prices to pay to maintain such a beautiful gown,' continued Rashid. 'But it didn't end there. Diderot began to notice that the rest of his home looked shabby in comparison to the gown. His existing clothes and dresses were threadbare and faded, in contrast to the rich colours of the gown. So he needed to replace them. He also used to sit in a straw chair. But his gown looked silly on such a cheap old chair. He bought a chair upholstered in rich Moroccan leather, with colours that suited the scarlet tones of his gown. Diderot often spent most of his day sitting at his desk, wearing the gown. Yet the gown didn't match the old desk. So he purchased a new expensive desk. Once he had that desk, his paintings looked amateurish and faded. He needed more exquisite art on his walls, art that matched the newly acquired desk and drapes. And very soon, Diderot plunged into debt.'

'When Diderot realised his mistake, he wrote the essay "Regrets on Parting with My Old Dressing Gown." In the essay he said, *I was the absolute master of my old robe. I have become the slave of the new one.*

'Now come to the present day. When you buy a new home, you would need new furniture to fill and decorate your home. When you buy a new phone, then you need to get a new case; probably a good one. When you buy a new sofa set, you would then need a new dining table which would match with your sofa to bring conformity in your possessions and give a uniform picture of your wealth and life-style. When you buy a new shirt, then you need a matching pair of jeans or a new blazer, which would go well with your shirt. So people jump into an escalator to upgrade themselves without realising that they are eroding their savings and are going out of their budget and very soon they fall into debt just like Denis Diderot had. This phenomenon is now called as *Diderot Effect*.'

If you want to become rich, you should not succumb to Diderot Effect. You should purchase only those items which you really need and not those others expect you to buy. Because it is not others; but you who will have to pay for those items. And if you continue to purchase those items just to upgrade yourself and/or which you do not need then very soon you will be left with no money to buy stuff which you would really need.

'So in the evening when you were enticing the gentleman to purchase a pair of jeans, you were using Diderot Effect,' said Vinay.

'Correct. That is my job; it is my business to bring people to buy stuff from my shop. Yet it is their job to decide whether they need to purchase or not. *Remember, someone's expense is income for someone else.* If that gentleman would not have spent his money then I would not have generated income for myself. So, I being a businessman was just doing my duty,' said Rashid with a smile.

Vinay understood what Rashid was trying to convey. He made a promise to himself that he would never succumb to *Diderot Effect.* He smiled silently for he had learnt the principles of building a strong defence.

Vinay's eyes opened upon hearing the announcement from the Air Hostess that the plane is ready to land in San Francisco. He cleaned his eyes and drank some water from the bottle placed in a pouch in front of him. The magazine that he was reading before he went to sleep was still open on the tray. As he was about to close the magazine and put it in the pouch, he glanced over an article which read: 'Reliance to enter into 4G: Reliance Jio is born.' He read the article and then put it back in the pouch and thought, *The Richest Man in India is still creating additional sources of income for himself.*

Eight

THE GOOD, THE BAD AND
THE UGLY

Vinay returned to Bengaluru in the first week of February. He had a hectic schedule at his company's HQ and barring for few weekends when he had gone with his US colleagues to visit in and around California, he was mainly involved in his work for the entire period of his stay.

After a week from his return, Vinay met Ajay and discussed with him about his learning from his football coach – Imran Rashid – during their college days. Ajay was surprised to know that not only Rashid Sir was a businessman but he was so financially literate as well. He thanked Vinay for letting him know how to create a great offence and a strong defence. He really liked Diderot Effect and was able to relate how he has been a victim of it since he started to earn. Ajay also liked the concept of 'protecting you from yourself.' He said that it was very similar to 'pay yourself first' strategy to which Vinay smiled.

Ajay then told Vinay that he would be going to Allahabad next month to attend his cousin – Rajesh's wedding – will not be able to meet with him during the period. He told him further that once he returns, he would call him and continue his journey of financial literacy from him. Vinay smiled and told Ajay to convey his wishes to his cousin.

Ajay and Priya were greeted by Ajay's father when they alighted from the Poorva Express at the Allahabad station. Ajay's father immediately took his granddaughter from Ajay's arms to kiss her on her forehead and cheeks. Both Ajay and Priya touched his feet while he showered blessings on both of them. Ajay's father then asked his granddaughter how she has been doing, to which his princess started to cry as she tried to jump to her mother. Once Priya took Kiara in her arms, the crying stopped. Then they started to move towards the station exit to take a taxi for home.

'Actually, she doesn't recognise you well Papa. That's why she had started to cry,' said Priya.

'I know. It's my fault only. I should have gone to meet my granddaughter at least during Diwali last year. Anyway, how was the journey? Hope you all didn't have much problem?'

'No, not at all,' said Ajay. 'In fact Kiara was thrilled to travel in the train. It was her first train journey and most of the time, either she was sleeping or looking at the trees and mountains running behind the train.'

Ajay's father hurried past the group of auto drivers and taxi drivers that surrounded the exit gate of the station, who were busy looking for their prospective customers. He went straight to a particular cab. The driver promptly ran towards him and took the briefcase from him and put it in the cab's boot. Then at the direction of Ajay's father, he took the suitcase and bag from Ajay and put them gently in the boot after Ajay told him that there were few fragile items in the bag. Priya was holding her bag and thermos containing milk for Kiara in her arms and refused to part with them when the driver asked her for them.

'She might feel hungry on the way and then I would have to feed her. It's better I keep the thermos,' said Priya.

Knowing that taxi drivers at the station charge exorbitant fare, Ajay's father had arranged for a taxi beforehand. After all the items were kept and once everyone took their seats, the taxi took them home.

Ajay noticed how in a span of two years, things have changed in his city. The number of vehicles running on the road had increased exponentially. Small shops had made ways for bigger complexes. New and taller buildings had come up in some parts of the city. Also, some new hotels with flashing names had replaced the older ones.

'So, many people would have come for the occasion?' asked Ajay.

'Yes, almost all our relatives have come and few would be arriving by tomorrow,' said his father.

Ajay was thinking that it would be the first time Kiara would be meeting many of her relatives. She had heard about her *Chachas, Mamas and Mausis* but had never met them. Ajay and Priya had decided that it would be the best time to visit as they would be able to meet many of their relatives whom they also had not met for a long time. Also, it would give Ajay some break after he had gone through a series of job interviews and finally had got a job from an American chip making company in Bengaluru. Ajay had bargained for some time to join the company since he had to visit his native town to attend his cousin's wedding to which the company had agreed.

When they reached home, it was like a festive season. People were busy preparing for the ceremony. While girls were busy putting *mehndi* on their hands, kids were having a gala time among themselves. Everyone was delighted to see Ajay, Priya and Kiara. Ajay's mother took them to their room and asked about their well-being and how Kiara has been doing. Kiara first hesitated in going to her grandmother's lap but after Priya explained that she is her Daadi, she went to her grandmother's arms reluctantly.

After theirs bath they had lunch. All three of them went to take a nap.

'You all should go and rest. The train journey is very tiring' his mother had said when she was serving them lunch.

Once they woke up in the evening, both Ajay and Priya presented shirts, pants, sarees and salwar suits to their relatives, which they had purchased in Bengaluru's Commercial Street and Chikpet market. Ajay's mother then asked Priya if she has brought any jewellery to wear during the marriage ceremony. Priya then took out a red box and showed her the necklace and earrings which she had received as her marriage gift from one of the relatives from Ajay's side.

'You will wear this?' said her mother-in-law a little surprised. 'If you wear this then the person who had gifted this to you would tell everyone that we don't have money to buy new jewellery. Besides this one doesn't suit your status. After all both of you are engineers and earning decently. Why would my *bahu* wear anything less than others?'

Priya was short of words for some time. She could not say anything to her mother-in-law. Only Ajay and she knew how difficult it had been for them in the past few months. They had not disclosed about Ajay's layoff to either of their parents, thinking that it would further aggravate their problem. Possibly their parents would be stressed unnecessarily.

'Actually Mummyji, we have used most of our savings as a down payment for our new apartment in Bengaluru. After that we didn't have much left to purchase jewellery,' replied Priya after some time.

'Yes, I understand that. But still.'

Ajay entered the room while the conversation was going on. Ajay's mother then told him about the problem. She told him to go and buy necklace and a pair of earrings for Priya today only.

'Nobody will notice what Priya is wearing. It's made of gold only. It's not an artificial one,' said Ajay.

'See, you all should be buying some amount of gold jewellery every year, particularly during *Akshaya Tritya* and *Dhanteras* as buying jewellery during these days bring prosperity to us. Just like home, these are our assets, which will help us during rainy days. You know, the price of gold rises all the time. Family marriages are a perfect time to buy some jewellery. You should go today evening itself with Priya to get her a new gold set – necklace and earrings. I will look after Kiara. If you don't have money then I will ask your father to lend you some,' said his mother.

'No, no. We have sufficient money with us. You don't need

to tell it to Papa. We will go and get the jewellery today.'

Thinking that he would not be spending his money and would be purchasing an asset only, Ajay went with Priya to a local shop and after looking through a range of designs finally zeroed in for a necklace and a pair of earrings.

The marriage ended ceremoniously. Ajay had danced enthusiastically for his cousin and Kiara took much delight seeing her father dance to the tune of latest Bollywood hits. After the post-marriage rituals were over, relatives had started leaving for their respective homes.

Soon, it was time for them to leave. Almost all of their family members had come to the station to see them off. Kiara had bonded well with her grandfather and uncles during the past ten days. Now she felt at ease with all of them. Once the TTE waived the green flag as the train started to move after a deafening whistle blew, both Ajay and Priya waved from their coaches in response to the waving of hands by their family knowing full well that their family could not seeing them behind the tinted window glass pane.

The 21st April 2015 was a holiday in Karnataka. Ajay had been busy in his new office and had been working late night attending conference calls from his team seated at US and UK. Today being *Akshaya Tritya* he slept a little longer and even after getting up he remained in the bed playing with his little daughter. Priya after instructing the maid about the breakfast had returned to the bedroom and indulged herself with her husband and daughter.

'Hey, today is *Akshaya Tritya*. We should go and buy some jewellery. Remember what Mummyji had said in our last trip,' said Priya getting up from bed.

'Yes, I remember that.' Ajay was still playing with Kiara.

After getting the pay cheques from his new company, Ajay's confidence had once again revived. He remembered his mother's words and realised that for the past two years he hadn't purchased any jewellery for Priya except for the one, which he had purchased in Allahabad just before his cousin's marriage. He thought of doing so today. And today being an auspicious day to purchase jewellery further fuelled his wish for buying a gold bracelet for his wife and daughter.

When Ajay and Priya were coming out from the jewellery shop, they met Vinay and his family who were returning from a temple nearby. They all greeted and wished happiness and prosperity to each other. Ajay then informed Vinay about his new job and company.

'Hey Congrats! But you didn't tell last time when we met about your new job,' said Vinay.

'Actually, it slipped my mind,' said Ajay.

'So, where is the party?'

'Anytime, anywhere,' said Ajay smilingly.

'So, what were you doing here?'

'Today is Akshaya Tritya so we thought of buying some jewellery for us.'

'Did you buy jewellery because of some need or just because it was Akshaya Tritya?' asked Vinay.

'I thought today is an auspicious day to purchase jewellery. This will bring prosperity to our home,' said Ajay defending himself to which Vinay smiled in response.

'Any plans for weekend? If you are free then why don't you come home,' said Vinay.

'Sure,' replied Ajay. He knew that Vinay has something to

share with him and was happy that he would learn something new from him.

When Ajay went over the next weekend, Vinay was busy drawing some pictures in his notepad. Vinay asked Ajay to sit on the chair beside him; while he got up and went to his *almirah* to fetch a letter from his father that he handed to Ajay.

Dear Son,

There are three types of assets that people acquire/buy in their lifetime. I call them Good Assets, Bad Assets and Ugly Assets. I define them as below:

Good Assets: *These assets put money into your wallet with rate of return greater than the inflation rate. These appreciate in value with time and can be sold easily in the market to realise the monetary gain.*

Bad Assets: *These assets don't put money into your wallet but helps you reduce your expense. In case they put money into your wallet, their rate of return is less than inflation rate. And if you try to sell them in the market you might have to incur losses.*

Ugly Assets: *These assets don't put money into your wallet. Rather they take away money from your wallet. Further, these assets depreciate in value with time and if sold in the market, it would definitely bring losses to you.*

To help you understand the difference between the good, bad and ugly assets, I have drawn a simple box diagram at the back of the letter. I hope it will increase your understandings of the different types of assets.

Now to become rich, all you need to do is purchase as many Good Assets as possible. While rich people acquire good assets, middle-class keep themselves busy acquiring bad and ugly assets. Poor people don't have the money to purchase any assets. **So, all I want you to do is simply spend your life purchasing Good Assets – then nobody can stop you from becoming rich.**

Lovingly yours,
Ram Prasad

Ajay then turned over the letter. He saw the following diagram.

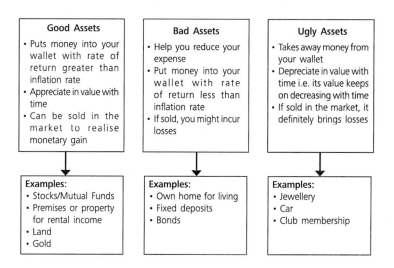

Good Assets	Bad Assets	Ugly Assets
• Puts money into your wallet with rate of return greater than inflation rate • Appreciate in value with time • Can be sold in the market to realise monetary gain	• Help you reduce your expense • Put money into your wallet with rate of return less than inflation rate • If sold, you might incur losses	• Takes away money from your wallet • Depreciate in value with time i.e. its value keeps on decreasing with time • If sold in the market, it definitely brings losses
Examples: • Stocks/Mutual Funds • Premises or property for rental income • Land • Gold	**Examples:** • Own home for living • Fixed deposits • Bonds	**Examples:** • Jewellery • Car • Club membership

Ajay turned over the letter and read it again. He tried to grasp what was written in the letter but somehow found it confusing that while Gold was classified as Good Asset, Jewellery was grouped into Ugly Asset. Also he was thinking that probably Vinay's father had made a mistake in putting *Own Home* as bad asset, though he had rightly classified *premises or property for rental income* as good asset. He put forth his queries to Vinay, who – before he answered, shared a visual from a PPT presentation that he showed to Ajay.

Asset

Liability

'Remember, what we had discussed earlier,' said Vinay 'that an asset is something, which puts money into your wallet. The more money it puts with lesser capital/principal amount, the better is the asset. Liability on the other hand takes away money from your wallet in the form of interest and principal payment. Hence more assets you have, the fatter your wallet will be while the more liabilities you have, the thinner your wallet will be.'

'Yes, I remember that,' said Ajay recalling his discussion with Vinay in the park during which he had learnt that surplus helps in creating asset and deficit leads to increase in liabilities.

'So, coming to your question that why gold is a good asset and jewellery is an ugly asset; let me answer it by asking you a question,' said Vinay. 'How much do you pay when you are purchasing some gold jewellery?'

'I pay for the weight of the gold times the price per unit of gold.'

'I wished it was like that. Sadly this is not true! The world is not what we are made to believe it to be. Don't you think that you pay something more?' asked Vinay.

'Yes, the making charges.'

'What is the amount of making charges?'

'It ranges from 15% to 20%. Yet isn't it the jeweller's right to ask for making charges. After all, they spend their time and effort for designing and creating jewellery for us,' said Ajay.

'Probably you should know that jewellers don't make much money in selling gold to you. They make money by levying the making and wastage charges on their customers when they sell them the jewellery.'

Vinay paused for some time and then continued 'So, when you are purchasing jewellery by paying ₹120 to the jeweller, the actual value of jewellery that you get is ₹100 only. And by doing this, you are breaking one of the fundamental rules of wealth creation.'

'And what is that?' asked Ajay.

'*You should purchase an asset at its value or lower than its value because money is made at the time of purchase of the asset. When you sell the asset, you are simply realising the monetary gain made from the purchase of the asset at the right value,*' said Vinay.

'You should also understand the difference between value of an asset and its price,' continued Vinay. 'Value is something which the asset commands because of its intrinsic nature and price is what the buyer is agreeing to pay for the asset. *You as an investor should always look at the value of an asset and not its price and should never pay more than the value of the asset that you are purchasing.*'

'Have you ever asked the jeweller what happens in case you wish to sell the jewellery back to them?' asked Vinay.

'In that case, they would refund an amount equivalent to the rate of gold times the weight of the gold,' replied Ajay.

'So assuming the gold rate to remain same, they would be paying ₹100 to you for the jewellery for which you had paid an amount of ₹120 which will lead to a direct loss of 20% for you. Jewellery, like a car, depreciates by more than 20% to 30% the moment they are out of the shop or showroom and that is why I put them in ugly assets. They never put money into your wallet, rather they take away money from your wallet in the form of making [wastage] charges and locker charges for jewellery; and in the form of petrol, maintenance charge, insurance, road tax and registration tax for car. The *ugly assets* behave very much in the same way as liabilities since they take away money from your wallet. That's why you should keep them to the extent of your necessity and never purchase them thinking that you are buying an asset.'

Ajay realised how he had been foolish when he bought jewellery. He also recalled how his parents also made the same mistakes when they used to purchase jewellery with the thought that they had gained assets.

'Though I now understand that jewellery is an ugly asset, but how is gold a good asset?' asked Ajay.

'Any asset which brings money to your pocket, appreciates in value with time and can be sold in the market to realise monetary gain is called good asset. Let us consider gold, first understand how gold derives its value – how its price is determined,' said Vinay.

Ajay was listening to Vinay very attentively. He never had understood the reasons for high price of gold.

'The value of an asset is the cash flow it produces during its lifetime, reckoned at present value,' said Vinay. 'In simple words, it is the present value of the cash flows that the asset would produce. Different assets produce different types of cash flows. Bonds and Fixed Deposits provide interest plus the principal amount at the time of maturity. Stocks produce dividends at regular intervals and rental of real estate provides you with rent every month. But what cash flow does gold give – typically nothing. Further, most assets and commodities have some or other use. For example, steel is used in construction industry; copper in making wires etc. But what use does the gold have and what is its value? Typically gold does nothing apart from sitting and looking pretty. It doesn't have any industrial, scientific or medical applications. It does not generate energy like wood or coal, neither is it used in transmission of any energy. So, there is no practical use of gold apart from the sparkle that it radiates. So why is it so costly?' asked Vinay.

Ajay looked at Vinay without answering.

'It's because of our belief that the price of gold will go up in the future and then we will be able to sell it at a higher price to someone else. This practice is also called a *greater fool theory,* which states that the price of an object is determined not by its intrinsic value but by irrational beliefs and expectations of market participants, namely the buyers. A price can be justified by a rational buyer under the belief that another party is willing to pay an even higher price or one may rationally have the expectation that the item can be resold to a "greater fool!" later.

'It is because of the non-corrosive nature of the gold and its purity that people believe that its value will never go down. The gold does not corrode when exposed to air and neither does it dissolve when mixed with water. However, it is dense and malleable, which means it can easily be moulded into different shapes. However just like any commodity, the price of gold is also determined by the market forces of demand and supply,' continued Vinay. 'Generally, when the economy is doing well most investors will put their money in stocks to take benefit of the growth of economy and consequently demand of gold will come down and as a result its price drops. When the investors lose their trust in the economy they will start to put their money in gold that results in an increase in its demand and hence higher price.'

'So, if the price of gold can come down then why should it be classified as Good Asset?' asked Ajay.

'Because if you look over a period of around four–five years, more often than not the price of gold has appreciated more than the inflation rate and that is why it is a good asset. Further, it acts as a hedge against the general mood of the economy because whenever the economy is down and stock market declines, the price of gold rises for most of the time. So, if you have a portfolio of Good Assets comprising of Stocks, Mutual Funds, Gold etc. then even in case of decline in stock market, your overall value of portfolio will not come down since the drop in value of stocks would have easily been compensated for by the increase in prices of the gold. Additionally, unlike jewellery, which people are not able to sell because of emotional attachment, the gold in the form of bar or coins can be sold very easily in the market to realise monetary gain and that is why it is termed as a Good Asset.'

While Ajay was thinking about the difference between gold and jewellery, Ananya brought tea and snacks for both. Ajay greeted her with a *Namaste* and asked her about her job. Ananya then wished good luck to Ajay for his new job and left the room to look after her kids.

While sipping the tea, Ajay relooked at the letter. He felt uncomfortable seeing that House for own living was classified as Bad Asset and after giving some more thoughts he thought it to be better to get it clarified from Vinay himself.

'Does your own home in which you live bring any money to your wallet?' asked Vinay.

'No,' said Ajay.

'Does it appreciate in value over the time?'

'Yes.'

'But, can you sell it in the market to realise the monetary gain because it has appreciated in value?'

'No,' replied Ajay.

'Since your own home for living doesn't bring any money to your wallet and since you cannot sell it in the market to realise the monetary gain because you need a roof for your family, your home for living is not a Good Asset,' said Vinay smilingly.

Ajay was dumbfounded for a second as he now realised that what he was considering his greatest asset – in which he has put all his and his wife's savings was nothing but a Bad Asset. He thought for some time and then spoke, 'And what about the second home from which we get rental income?'

'I would rather call it a real estate than a home; because there is always one home and you need only one home to live. The second/third home, which generally people talk about should be treated as a real estate property and not home. Now coming to the point; does your property, which you have let out to the tenants bring money to your wallet?' asked Vinay.

'Yes. In the form of rental income every month,' said Ajay.

'Does it appreciate in value over time?'

'Yes'

'Can you sell it in the market to realise the monetary gain from its appreciated value and then reinvest the gain in some other good assets or use the monetary gain to fulfil your certain desires?'

'Yes,' replied Ajay.

'See, you yourself has answered why your real estate properties which you have let out for rental income is a good asset,' said Vinay. 'Whenever you think to buy an asset just ask these three questions about that asset:

- Will it bring money to your wallet?
- Will it appreciate in value with time?
- Can it be sold in the market easily to realise the monetary gain?

If answer to all the three questions is 'Yes,' then that asset is a Good Asset. You should definitely buy that asset. However, if the answer to any of the questions is 'No,' then you should first decide the utility value of that asset and then decide – wisely – whether to purchase that asset or not. In case you decide to purchase that asset because of its utility value that you require then always bear in mind that it is either a Bad or an Ugly Asset you plan to buy.'

Ajay was thoughtful after listening to Vinay who had got

up to fetch a glass of water for himself. He offered Ajay some water. After quenching his thirst, Ajay thought about all his assets that he has acquired till now and realised that almost all of his assets were either Bad Assets or Ugly Assets.

'Coming to the asset, which is most dear to everyone – your own home, which most people consider as their most prized asset, what if I tell you that your own home is not an asset but a liability, then how would you feel,' asked Vinay.

'Probably, I would say that you are wrong,' said Ajay.

Vinay smiled for a while and then spoke 'Now that you have purchased an apartment for yourself, how did you make the payment? Did you pay the entire amount from your pocket or did you avail loan from some Bank or Housing Finance Company?'

'I paid 20% of the price from my savings and for the balance 80%, I took home loan from a bank,' said Ajay.

'So, in this case you have only 20% ownership of your house as 80% is owned by the Bank from which you have taken loan. Since you are making an EMI payment every month, your home, which is not exactly owned by you is taking away money from your wallet and therefore it is not an asset but a liability for you.'

Vinay paused for some time to let the idea sink in Ajay's mind. He observed Ajay who was thinking deeply. Seeing that no question came from Ajay's side, Vinay spoke 'in addition to the EMI payment that you make every month you also pay property tax every three months as well as you have maintenance charges to be paid to the society/association in addition to insurance expense and utility charges like water and electricity bill. Hence, your own home behaves very much similar to a liability because it takes away money from your wallet continuously. And to top it all, your own home is not yours till you have paid off your home loan entirely. Till the time you have home loan outstanding against your name, your own home is not your property, rather it is the property of the bank, which has extended a loan to you. It is their asset and not yours.'

'What is the tenure of the home loan that you have taken?' asked Vinay.

'It is twenty years,' said Ajay in a low voice.

'You know, what is the biggest irony of the middle-class?'

'What?' Ajay answered by questioning Vinay.

'*The biggest irony of the middle-class is that all throughout their life they work very hard to purchase an asset, which they never own*. Only when they reach their retirement age and if they have been able to pay all their EMIs on time that they become the actual owner of their home. For twenty to thirty years of their life when they are at the peak of their productivity, the middle-class keep working hard just to pay the bank on time thinking that they are making payment for their asset, which is actually the asset of the bank because this home is bringing money to the bank in the form of monthly EMIs. **Remember, owning a home is great. But the key is: owning it free and clear**. If you have loans against your home then you do not own it; rather the bank owns it because majority of the payment has been made by them. It is their assets and not yours.'

'The greatest loss of purchasing an expensive home for self-living is the missed opportunities' continued Vinay. 'Most of the middle-class people will put their entire life saving to purchase their dream home. And if they are high income middle-class, they will purchase a three bedroom or four bedroom apartment in a posh locality or a row house or even a villa. And after they have made such a purchase, they don't have anything left to invest in Good Assets which would have brought further income to them because most of their earnings go in making the monthly EMI payments to Bank.'

'But rich people will never put their entire savings for purchase of their own home. They know that Own Home is a Bad Asset and hence they put only a portion of their savings in buying home as per their requirement. With the balance fund available, they invest in Good Assets like Stocks, Businesses, a second real estate property for rental income, which brings further income to them and that is the reason rich people become richer. If rich people want to move to a bigger house, first they build an asset column which then produces regular cash flows. And then with the income generated from their Good Assets, they buy luxuries – that is they move in to a bigger and better house. Remember, *rich people buy luxuries last while the poor and middle-class buy luxuries first.*'

'Take my example. First I bought a two bedroom apartment for myself and also invested in another property, which brings rental income to me. This second property is bringing regular cash flows to me every month with which I have been able to close my existing home loan much before its schedule. And now that I have surplus, I am planning to move to a three bedroom apartment by selling the present home. I don't need to exert myself as I still have my second property, which would be bringing rental income to me every month.'

'Remember *if you really want to become rich, you should purchase your luxuries from the income generated from your asset column and not from your regular income.* Your regular income should go towards building your asset column and then meeting your monthly expenses. And that is why I first purchased a two bedroom apartment. Once income from my asset column started producing enough money, now I am planning to move to a bigger house. This luxury of a bigger house is not being met from my regular income but the income generated from the asset column.'

'If purchasing a home for own use is such a wasteful expense, then why should anybody buy a home?' asked Ajay.

'I am not saying that you should not buy a home for your living. In fact, you must have a home for yourself as it brings numerous benefits to you,' said Vinay.

'And what are those benefits?'

'First and foremost, it helps you in bringing down your expense. Now that you are living in your home, you do not need to pay any rent, which you would otherwise have to pay to your landlord. Since, reducing your expense is better than increasing your income; I classify the home as an asset and not as a liability. Yet I still put it as a Bad Asset for reasons I explained to you earlier. Second, owing a home gives you a sense of security, a sense of stability. Once you own a home, you will never get a notice that you have to vacate the home. Your kids will never have to change schools unnecessarily. Third, having your own home gives a pride of ownership. You can paint the wall with the colour of your choice. You can remodel your house according to your need, attach permanent fixtures and decorate your home according to your desires. Your kids can even draw their imaginations on the wall of your home if you allow them to, which cannot happen in a rented home. Fourth, it gives you a freedom to pursue other goals in life. *Owning a home is the first and most important goal of any person. Once that has been achieved after you have paid off your entire loan, you start chasing your other goals because now you are not burdened with paying off your rent/EMI.*

'And if you notice the benefits that I have just explained, you would see that most of these benefits are intangible benefits, i.e. these benefits you cannot measure directly in terms of monetary gain. Nonetheless, these benefits help you lead a complete life enjoying every aspect and happiness that life has to offer. And that is why, owning a house is a must for everyone. Yet in doing so, you should not commit the mistake that most people do which is putting their entire life savings into purchasing the home. Rather, you should follow what rich people do. You should put only a portion of your savings into your home and the balance amount, you can invest in good Assets, which would bring further income to you. And once income from your assets starts increasing then you can move to a bigger and better home.

'If you ask an average middle-class person, how much of their total net worth is invested in their home, they will tell that 80% to 90% of their net worth is in home and the balance in fixed deposits and jewellery. But if you look at the rich people, you will realise that their own home comprises of not more than 25% to 30% of their net worth with the balance amount of 70% to 75% being invested in good assets such as stocks, mutual funds, businesses, gold, land, real estate,' said Vinay.

Ajay tried to recall his net worth and its share in his newly purchased apartment and was shocked to realise that around 80% of his net worth was invested in his home and the balance 20% in fixed deposits, car and jewellery. He felt very guilty that almost all his savings were invested in either bad or ugly assets. Now he promised himself that he would improve his financial condition to start acquiring good assets and keep bad and ugly assets as minimum as possible.

'Most people don't understand why they struggle financially because they don't understand the cash flow,' continued Vinay. 'These people are highly educated, professionally successful but financially illiterate. But *Rich people are always financially literate even though they may not be highly educated.* Rich people know that *money is like a flow of water and if you do not control its flow then it will find its own way,* which always results in waste. Hence, Rich people focus distinctly on the flow of money, that is cash flow to control its flow in their favour.'

Vinay then got up from his chair and brought three sheets of diagrams which he was working on before Ajay had come. He then handed the first sheet to Ajay.

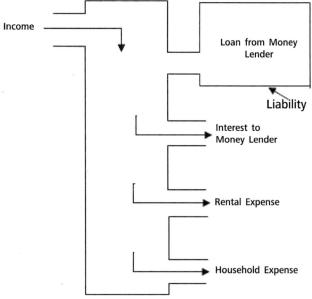

Diagram: *Cash Flow of Poor People*

'This is the cash flow of poor people,' said Vinay while Ajay was looking carefully at the diagram. 'Income, just like water – flows into the tube and then goes out from various outlets as expenses. If you notice, poor people's entire income is spent to meet their expenses. In most of the cases, they fall short of money and hence avail loan from money lenders which leads to creation of liability for them. Since interest charged by money lenders is very high, most of their income then goes as interest to the money lenders leaving them with little money to pay for the rent as well as their household expense.

This is how they get trapped in a vicious circle from which most of them are never able to come out in their lifetime. Also, observe that the tube ends after meeting their expenses which simply means that they don't have any surplus left which otherwise could have been used to create assets.'

Vinay then handed over the second sheet to Ajay. Ajay looked carefully at the diagram. (Diagram seen overleaf on page 170)

'This is the cash flow diagram of a typical middle-class person,' said Vinay. 'In this case, there is an additional expense outlet viz. Income Tax which for most of them is in the range of 20 to 30% of their income. Additionally in case of middle-class, after meeting their expenses, people create assets, which are mostly Bad Assets and Ugly Assets.'

Vinay then handed him the third diagram; the cash flow diagram of the rich people. (Diagram seen on page 171)

'Rich people after receiving their income and paying their income tax first allocate a portion of their money for buying Good Asset and then use the balance amount for their household expenses,' said Vinay. 'They know that money is like a stream of flowing water and if it is not controlled then it will find its

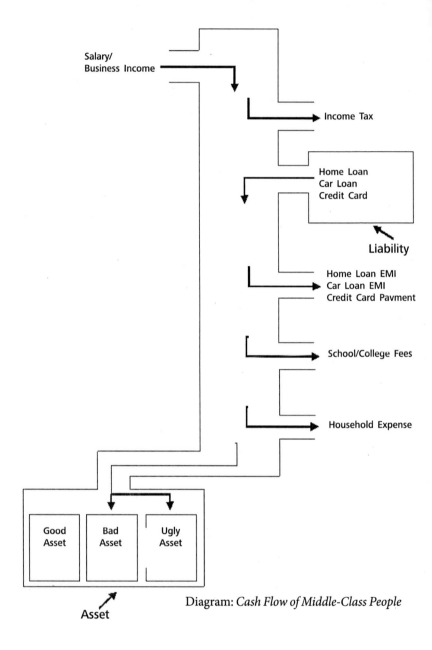

Diagram: *Cash Flow of Middle-Class People*

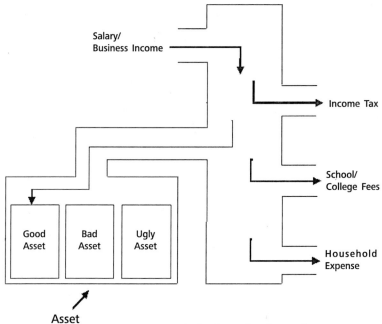

Diagram: *Cash Flow of Rich People*

own way. That is why Rich people always first divert a portion of their money towards Good Assets so that money is not wasted,' Vinay paused for a while and then asked 'Do you know the real beauty of the cash flow of rich people?'

'No,' said Ajay, who was observing the simplicity of the cash flow of the rich people over the cash flow of the middle-class people.

Vinay then took the diagram from Ajay's hand, drew a line over it and then handed the diagram to him.

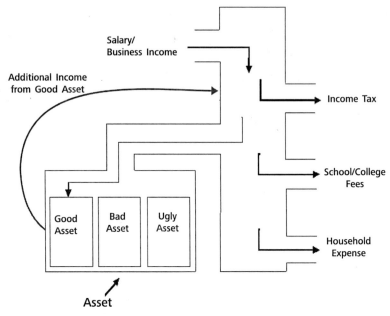

Diagram: *Additional Income from Good Assets*

'This additional income from Good Assets is the real beauty of the cash flow of rich people,' said Vinay pointing at the arrow originating from the Good Asset box. 'This helps the Rich people become richer and richer over time. The only difference between the cash flow of rich people and middle-class people is the allocation of their money into different assets and timing of the allocation.'

Vinay then took out another piece of paper and drew a table on it.

Rich People	Middle-Class People
Put money in good assets	Put money in bad and ugly assets
Put a specific amount of income in Asset box before using it for other household expenses	Put money in asset box with whatever is left over after meeting the monthly expense

'If you have observed one small but important message from the cash flows, it is that rich people are following the *Pay Yourself First* strategy and that is one of the main reason why they are rich,' said Vinay.

Ajay was smiling as he had understood the difference between good assets, bad assets and ugly assets. He also praised Vinay in his mind as he thanked him for making him financially literate.

Focus on Your Net Worth and not Your Income

'Do you know the law of attraction that was made popular by the author Rhonda Byrne in her book *The Secret*?' asked Vinay.

'Yes, the law, which tells that "like attracts like," i.e. whatever we focus on we bring to our life and that it expands,' Ajay recalled his discussion with Manisha where she referred the law several times.

'Correct. I have found this to be extremely helpful,' said Vinay. 'Have you ever noticed how most of the people talk about money? Whenever somebody wants to know how well someone is doing in his/her life or how well they are progressing, they would ask questions like "How much money do you make?" Your relatives, friends and parents would ask you "What is your take-home salary?" Even during lunch hour at your office or at the time of a smoke-break your colleagues would ask you "How much increment did you get this year?!" Seldom would they ask questions like "What is your net worth?" "How much money have you saved, invested and accumulated?"

'True. We often have discussions surrounding our salary, increment, promotion etc.'

'But if you go to some Business Conclave where Promoters and CXOs of the company come or if you happen to visit some Country Club, you will notice that their financial discussion always centres around Net Worth and not on Income. You will hear people talking like "Mr Chandra sold his stock options; he is worth over ₹20 crores"; "Mrs Shaw's company just went public and shares of her company were oversubscribed. She's worth ₹80 crores now"; "Mr Kumar's company was acquired by an MNC giant. He's over ₹50 crores"; "Mr Shah invested in a technology start-up which has been doing great. His investment would have made him over ₹10 crores." All these discussions focus on only one thing; their Net Worth. In a gathering of rich people, you will never get to hear "even after giving my 100% – working day and night, my salary increased by only 15%" *Rich people never focus on their income; they focus on their net worth.*'

'But to build the net worth you need to have an income. Without income, you cannot create a net worth for yourself. Also, the rich people discuss about net worth probably because they have such a huge amount of income that they don't need to focus on income and hence focus entirely on net worth,' said Ajay.

'Before I clarify your doubt, I hope you appreciate the fact that *the true measure of your wealth is your net worth and not your income.* It was always there and will always be. When we say someone is rich, we are not referring to his income but his net worth. If you search "Richest Man in India," in all probability you will get the list comprising of people like Mukesh Ambani, Dilip Shanghvi, Azim Premji among others with their net worth mentioned at the side of their name.' Vinay then took out his laptop, searched "Richest Man in India" on Google and then clicked on the first link which took him to the Forbes website.

Forbes India's 100 Richest People Rankings 2014				
Rank	Name	Net Worth	Age	Origin of Wealth
1	Mukesh Ambani	$23.6 Billion	58	Petrochemical, Oil & Gas
2	Dilip Shanghvi	$18.0 Billion	59	Pharmaceuticals
3	Azim Premji	$16.4 Billion	69	Software
4	Pallonji Mistry	$15.9 Billion	86	Construction

Vinay then showed the laptop to Ajay and said 'People are said to be rich; to be wealthy by their net worth and not by their income. If you look at the list, you will see the ranking to be based on their respective net worth. You will never see any mention of their income in the entire list and the article. So, always remember that *net worth is the true measure of wealth.* The more net worth you have the more rich you are and the more comfortable lifestyle you can have.'

'Remember, how we had defined net worth in our early discussions,' asked Vinay.

'Yes, net worth is the present value of total assets less liabilities' said Ajay.

'Now coming to your question that we need to have an income to create net worth, you should understand that income is just one of the three factors that determine your net worth. The other two factors are savings and investments. If you earn a good amount of income and spend it all or save very little, then you will not be able to create a good net worth for yourself. Only when you have savings and you put your savings into good assets that you will be able to build net worth. Rich people know that creating a high net worth is an equation which depends on all the three factors and hence they focus on net worth. *By focussing on net worth, rich people focus on all the three factors of the equation, namely Income, Savings and Investments.* Middle-class and the poor people on the other hand focus entirely on their Income. They do not focus on the other two factors; savings and investments and hence are not able to create wealth for themselves.'

'Have you ever gone fishing?' asked Vinay.

'No; never got a chance,' said Ajay.

'But you would have seen people fishing in movies or in Discovery channel on your TV.'

'Yes,' replied Ajay.

'Imagine that you are sitting beside a lake with a fishing rod and some bait. You catch fish, put them in the basket beside you and then focus on catching another fish. However, the basket that you are putting the fishes in is open and while you are focussing on catching the fish, a crane creeps in and starts relishing your fishes. After catching some 20–25 fish in say 2 hours, when you look into your basket you find that it is empty. Naturally you wonder where all the fish have gone. You know that they didn't swim back to the lake but they are gone. You can't find any other person nearby whom you could have thought stole your fish, so you go home dejected wondering where the fish went. This is the story of poor and middle-class. They keep focussing on earning income forgetting the fact that it is just one part of the chain. For making the chain complete you have to add savings and investments to your income and then only you will build a strong net worth for you.'

'Ever wondered how the Rich people would go for fishing?' asked Vinay.

'They would have covered the basket after putting the fish and then focus on catching another fish,' replied Ajay.

'Correct; the fish caught is your income but fish which is kept safe in the basket is like your net worth. What really matters is the number of fishes kept in the box and not the number of fish that you had caught,' said Vinay.

'In our earlier diagrams where we had drawn the cash flow, the net worth is nothing but the asset box less the liability box,' continued Vinay. 'The bigger the asset box and the smaller the liability box, the greater is your net worth... greater is your net worth, the wealthier and rich you become. So, when you focus on net worth, you automatically focus on entire chain comprising of income, savings and investments. As per the law of attraction, whatever you focus on expands and hence your net worth will expand. Remember, *rich people focus on their net worth and poor and middle-class people focus on their income.* And if you want to become rich, start focussing on your net worth.'

'How do we shift our focus from our income towards net worth?' asked Ajay.

'Start talking about your net worth with your friends and your wife. Keep a track of your net worth and check it every three months to see how it is progressing. Another simple way of focussing on your net worth is by measuring your success with your net worth. Middle-class people measure their success by their income. They get delighted and happy whenever their salary/income increases. However, *rich people measure their success by their net worth and not by their income.* For the purpose of wealth building, income doesn't matter much. Once you are in a high income bracket, say you are earning ₹10–15 lakhs per annum or more, it matters less how much more you make than what you do with what you already have.'

Work for yourself even if you are working for others

Seeing Ajay had grasped how focussing on net worth would help him in his journey to become rich and successful, Vinay spoke, 'Do you know what my father used to say?'

'What?' Ajay asked.

'He used to say, *learn to work harder on yourself than you would do on your job.*'

'And what does that mean?'

'It only means that *you should learn to work for yourself even if you are working for others,*' said Vinay.

'But, don't we work for ourselves?'

'Like I said earlier when we had discussed the Pay Yourself First strategy, most of the people work for everyone else but for themselves.'

'Yes, we had discussed this and also know how paying yourself first help us in bringing down the work that we do for others.'

'Correct! But there is one more thing that I want you to understand.'

'And what is that,' said Ajay with a smile.

'Do you know what the underlying motive of every company's business is?'

'I guess it is different for different companies. If a company sells toothpaste and hair oil, then their business is selling toothpaste and hair oil. Similarly, if a company sells mobiles and laptops then their business is selling mobiles and laptops. What is a big deal in this?' said Ajay a little surprised.

'What you are telling is just a means for them to achieve their underlying motive. The underlying motive of any company; the real business of any company is to make as much profit as possible and build a strong balance sheet as they can. The real joy and fun for any company is to make profit. They do not enjoy or have fun in selling toothpastes and toiletries to people. But they do enjoy and celebrate when their profit is more than their previous year figures or it is better than that of their nearest competitors.'

'Selling toothpaste, hair oil, mobiles and laptops is just a means to achieve their real target of making profit and creating a strong balance sheet. Ask any company, what is their mission or goal – they would answer that they want to become the number one company in their respective field. How do you become number one? It is when your total income, your net profit, your balance sheet is the best in the industry.'

'Just like every company has a business of their own, ever individual should also have their own business,' said Vinay.

'But, how can everyone have a business of their own. I for example, am working in an IT company. I am an employee. I cannot create my own company right now,' said Ajay.

'You do not need to create a company to have a business of your own. You can work for others and still work for yourself.'

'Sorry, I didn't get you.'

'You need to mind your own business. Just like a company's business revolves around its balance sheet, your business too should revolve around your balance sheet; your asset box. And just like selling toothpaste and toiletries help a company to mind its business of creating a strong balance sheet; getting salaries from your company helps you creating a strong balance sheet for you; a bigger asset box for yourself.'

'Remember, *earning salary is just a means for you. It should not be your goal. Your real goal should be to create a stronger balance sheet for yourself by increasing your asset box and decreasing your liability box.* Rich people understand this and that is why they focus on their asset box while everyone else focuses on their income statement.'

'While you may continue working for your company; you should always learn to mind your own business. If you focus only on your income then to increase your income you need to work hard; you need to slog and try to switch to another company which can give you a better salary. But doing so, you are not making yourself rich. You make the company whom you work for richer. Most of the people struggle financially because all throughout their life because they keep on minding someone else's business and making them rich.'

'The Rich and successful people see themselves as self-employed, no matter who signs their pay cheques. The biggest mistake you can ever make is to think that you work for anyone other than yourself. You are always self-employed. You are always the President of your own personal service corporation, no matter where you might be working at the moment. When you see yourself as self-employed, you see yourself as the boss of your own life. You see yourself as completely in charge of your physical health, your financial well-being, your career, your relationships, your lifestyle, your home, your car and every other element of your existence.'

'You mean to say that I can work for myself while I am still working for others,' said Ajay.

'Yes and that is what most of the rich people do. They mind their own business. They keep on working on their balance sheet while they continue working for others. You do not need to be an entrepreneur to mind your business. Keep your daytime job, but start saving and buying Good Assets and not liabilities. Keep expenses low, reduce liabilities and diligently build a base of solid assets. And once your asset box has become big; then you do not need to work for others any more, though you may still continue if you love your job. Your assets, by bringing in additional income will take care of your expenses. And then, you can be your own boss. Your assets become your employees who keep on bringing income to you even when you are asleep or have gone for some vacation to an exotic location in Australia or New Zealand. Just think! The bigger your asset box is, the bigger boss you become.'

Vinay waited for some time and observed Ajay who was thinking on whatever he had told him. Then he spoke to break Ajay's train of thoughts, 'You know, I have read it many times and have come across many such people in my real life. Probably, you would have heard it too. There are many people who are sincere and worked hard all their life yet still wind up broke and embarrassed. Once they retire or have certain liabilities to be fulfilled, they realise that they have nothing and that they are broke. These are the people their employers would have loved to be with them because all throughout their life they had kept their company's priorities on top of theirs. All throughout their life they had continued to mind their company's business but never had taken out time to mind their own business. Remember, if you do not want to be like them then *you've got to be better than a good worker. You've got to be better than sincere. You've got to be a good planner who minds his own business first before minding someone else's business.'*

'Let me tell you about one incident that forced me to change my thinking,' said Vinay. 'One evening, while returning from office I saw a billboard near a residential construction site which said: *'People who you are working for are waiting for you at home. Be safe.'* I thought about it for some time and then questioned myself, am I really working for my family who is waiting for me at home or am I working for my company and its clients. Am I really solving problems for my family or am I solving problems for my company and its clients? Am I creating a future for my family or am I creating future for my company and its clients?'

'Then I thought, well the company is paying me for my work. Then, I realised what is happening to my salary. Am I keeping it and saving it for me and my family's future or am I just paying others. Then all of a sudden, this old teaching came to my mind that 'God helps those who help themselves.' Since then I started helping myself first. I started working for myself.'

'Do you know that there's a technique which will help you know how much you work for yourself and how much you work for others?' said Vinay.

'And what is that?' asked Ajay.

'Suppose, there is a person whose monthly gross income is ₹45,000, which means in a week her earnings is ₹11,250. This person works for nearly 9 hours per day or 45 hours per week. What would be her hourly income? It would be ₹250 per hour of her work. Now suppose that this person didn't save a single rupee last week – that is she spent whatever she earned. In her kitty, there was nil money after 45 hours of work, which means she worked for zero hours for herself. She worked entirely 45 hours for someone else but not for herself.

'Now, suppose this same person saves ₹1000 in a week which is nearly 10% of her weekly gross income. This means, last week she worked for 4 hours for himself, (1000/250=4) which is less than an hour per day and balance 41 hours for someone else. It is up to you to decide how long you want to work for yourself – for how long you want to continue working for others.

'Now tell me, why any one shouldn't be working at least an hour a day for himself? Why not an hour and half or probably two hours per day? The problem is most people don't think in that way. The problem with most financial planning is that it focuses on numbers and not on people's lives; the hours; the period during which he is awake; the period during which he can spend time with his family. Instead of thinking just about numbers and income, think about hours of your life. How many hours are you planning to work for yourself this year, instead of working for your employer, the government, the credit card companies, the bank and everyone else who want a piece of what you earn? How many hours of this week do you think your future is worth?

'It seems to me that an hour a day is really not so much to ask in return for a bright future. If you're not saving that much of your income right now, you are working too much for others and not enough for yourself. You deserve better.

'Remember, just merely earning your salary doesn't mean you work for yourself. Only when you are able to save money from your salary and put it in proper investment tool which helps your money to grow in value with time, then you would be known as a person who works for himself. So the bottom line is this: *If you want to work more for yourself and less for others, increase the amount of your savings and put it in right places.*

'And yes last but not the least: *Only when you have a stronger balance sheet for yourself that you can create a stronger balance sheet for others.* You cannot help others if you are broke.'

Ajay was now lost in his thoughts. He never had viewed his income and saving in this way. He was now realising how foolish he had been in his entire career. He has been working for everyone else but for himself. He promised that he would start minding his own business from today itself and create a better future for himself and his family.

Meanwhile, Ananya called them for the dinner. Ajay looked at his watch and saw that it was already 45 minutes past 8. He immediately called Priya and informed her that he would have dinner at Vinay's place. He also told her to have dinner with Kiara as he would be late reaching home. Priya then told him that they had already had dinner since she knew that he would be coming home late. She asked him to be careful on his way home.

While they were moving towards the dining table, Ajay's mind was running a constant message '*Keep on acquiring good assets, focus on your net worth and start minding your own business, then you will never have any money problems.*'

Nine

THE HEALTHY WALLET

After his last visit to Vinay's home, Ajay had decided to invest a minimum of 20% of his salary in Good Assets which he would do immediately after receiving his salary so that he could follow the *Pay Yourself First* strategy. He opened a Trading and Demat account with one of the banks and had started investing in stocks, mutual funds, bonds and gold ETFs. He had realised that though fixed deposit offers a guaranteed income, the income earned on it was fully taxable and hence post-tax return from fixed deposits was hardly able to beat the inflation rate.

Soon three months had passed and it was time to file his income-tax return. Ajay had filled the income-tax return form and had filed it online. While returning from the nearby post office after dropping his signed income tax form, when he was about to reach his apartment, he suddenly fell down.

The security guard of the apartment complex immediately rushed to him; wrapped Ajay's arm around his shoulder and took him to the shade. He then called Priya on the intercom to ask her to come down immediately. Meanwhile, Ajay had gained consciousness however he was feeling very weak and had temperature running. Priya then drove Ajay to a nearby clinic. She asked the receptionist to arrange for a doctor.

Once the doctor had examined Ajay, he informed them that Ajay had suffered a minor heat stroke. Upon asking for its reason, the doctor told them that since it was very sunny today probably that Ajay did not have an adequate water intake before going out, that he suffered such a stroke. He also advised him to take proper diet comprising of carbohydrates, proteins, vitamins and minerals, which would take care of the requirements of the body. The doctor then prescribed certain vitamin tablets to Ajay to help him overcome weakness as he stressed the need to take good care of himself.

Ajay took leave for next two days from his office to take rest at home. While he was resting after his breakfast he thought of going through his income tax return file. He switched on his laptop and after checking for any new mails, opened his income tax file. After shutting down his laptop and keeping it on the table near his bed, Ajay started thinking how he can reduce his tax. He was paying nearly 25% of his gross salary as income tax and felt helpless because he could not think of any other possible ways to reduce his tax. He called Vinay and told him about his predicament. Vinay also told him that his income tax for this year was more than he had expected earlier. He then asked Ajay to meet him this weekend at his home.

Ajay met Vinay on Saturday early in the morning. He had regained his strength in the past five days and had rejoined his office.

'Do you remember Professor P Chakraborty?' asked Vinay.

'Yes, our professor of Signal Processing subject at NIT,' said Ajay.

'Correct. He has a friend here in Bengaluru; Mr Arnab Banerjee. I have arranged a meeting with him today. Would you be interested in joining me?'

'I have never heard of him. Who is he?' asked Ajay.

'He is the Assistant Commissioner of Income Tax in Bengaluru,' said Vinay with a smile.

'Great! Then what are we waiting for.'

Mr Banerjee was going through the morning newspaper when his doorbell rang. He welcomed both of them and asked them to take a seat in his living room. He then asked his maid to bring some water and tea for them, while he went inside his room and asked his kids to keep the volume of music low. His wife, a professor in a local college, had gone to conduct some extra classes.

Ajay was mesmerised by the sheer size of the living room and the garden that surrounded the house of Mr Banerjee. 'He must be very rich. He has such an impressive home.'

'It's not his house exactly. It is the government quarter provided by the central government. His own house is in Kolkata, which he has put on rent' said Vinay.

When Mr Banerjee entered the living room, both of them stood up. Mr Banerjee asked them to sit down and make themselves comfortable. He then asked them about his old friend P Chakraborty and told them that though both of them were school friends they are not able to keep in touch so regularly.

Mr Arnab Banerjee was in his late forties or early fifties. He had specs on his eyes and had strands of white hair over his ears. He had put on a comfortable kurta and pyjama, looking at ease, however was exuberant in his talk.

'So what brings you boys here?' asked Mr Banerjee.

'Sir, we both are working in IT companies here in Bengaluru. We make a decent earning for ourselves. However, our share of Income Tax is very high – we pay nearly 20% to 30% of our earnings as Income Tax. We take benefit of all the possible Income Tax deductions available to us such as 80C etc. but still huge amount of our income goes away as Income Tax. We are not able to do anything about it,' said Vinay.

'Well, that is the rule of the government. You cannot do anything about it. If you are earning then you have to pay income tax. You cannot evade that and if you try to evade that then I will send you a notice,' said Mr Banerjee with a smile.

'But Sir, there must be some ways in which we can reduce our income tax,' asked Ajay.

'And why do you want to reduce your income tax?' asked Mr Banerjee.

'Because whenever we take three steps forward, the income tax pulls us back by one step and after meeting our necessary expenses, we realise that we are not able to move even a fraction of a step and for most of the time we find that we are standing at the same place where we were a year back,' said Vinay. 'Actually, I feel Income Tax is not allowing us to make ourselves rich.'

'It is not income tax that is stopping you from becoming rich. It is you and only you who is stopping yourself from becoming rich. Income Tax is applicable to everyone but still there are many people who are very rich as also there are many more who are poor. So, you cannot blame income tax from stopping you from becoming rich.'

'I feel rich people do not pay income tax in the same proportion to their income as we pay. And we wanted to know if we can also do the same,' said Vinay.

Mr Banerjee now smiled. He had found just the student who asked the right questions to seek wisdom in the right direction. Many times before; he had people asking him how to reduce income tax – to which he had not entertained their queries seriously. Now he had one person who was asking the correct question that *rich people do not pay income tax in the same proportion of their income as normal people do.* And he thought he should answer this.

'Before I help you in your pursuit let me ask you one simple question,' said Mr Banerjee.

Both Ajay and Vinay were looking attentively at Mr Banerjee tying to absorb everything he was saying.

'What is your source of income?' asked Mr Banerjee.

'Our monthly pay cheque; our salary,' came the prompt reply from Ajay. Vinay smiled at the answer of Ajay as he knew what Mr Banerjee was up to.

'So, you are feeding your wallet with only your salary.'

'While a major part of my income comes from my salary, I have some fixed deposits, which give me interest income. Recently I have started to invest in stocks and mutual funds, which will give dividends. Yet still around 90% to 95% of my income comes from my salary,' said Ajay in a defensive tone.

'That means, you are keeping your wallet unhealthy. You are not feeding your wallet properly.'

'I didn't get it exactly about our wallet being unhealthy,' said Vinay. Ajay thanked Vinay in his mind because he too hadn't understood what Mr Banerjee was trying to convey.

'Like your body needs different essential nutrients such as proteins, vitamins, carbohydrates, minerals and water in right proportion; your wallet also needs income from different sources to remain healthy. If you don't feed your wallet with the income from right sources then it won't remain healthy; it will fall sick.'

'While I understand that different nutrients are not same and that they have different functions in our body, which helps to keep our body healthy, how come if we don't feed our wallet with right income sources, it falls sick. Isn't income from all sources the same?' asked Vinay.

'That is one of the greatest misconception most people have about money' said Mr Banerjee. '*All incomes are not equal. The amount of income that you get to keep in your wallet depends on their source, i.e. how they are generated.* In fact, the income tax department also asks you to declare different sources of income when you file your income tax return such as Income from salary or from your business, rental income, interest income, dividend income, capital gain etc. and all these incomes are taxed on different principle and at different rates. There are certain incomes such as salary or income from business for which you work and pay the highest tax; and there are incomes from other sources such as rental income, dividend income, capital gain etc. where you pay the minimum or sometimes no tax at all.'

Both Ajay and Vinay were realising the importance of what Mr Banerjee was saying. They knew that while their income from salary was taxed at the highest rate, the dividend income was not taxed at all.

'Now having told you that all incomes are not equal because the government and the income tax department treat income from different sources differently; let me ask you another question. What is required to generate income?'

'Our skill and expertise in some particular area and our hard work in that particular field generates income for us,' said Ajay.

'Correct. I guess you are missing something,' said Mr Banerjee.

'Our money invested in some correct places generates income for us,' said Vinay.

'Exactly; *Money begets more money*. Poor and middle-class people focus entirely on working hard to generate income. However, rich people know that with money they can generate more money without working hard for it and that is the reason they get richer. *While poor and middle-class people work hard for their money; rich people have their money work hard for them.*'

'So, you mean to say that working hard is not necessary to become rich,' asked Ajay.

'*Working hard in your area of expertise is important. But working hard alone will never make you rich*. If you look around yourself, you will see many people who are working very hard but not everyone is rich. Even if you look at people in your profession, you will see many people who work really hard, who would slog all day and night but still they are not rich. So, the idea that you have to work hard to get rich is fake and bogus.'

'But there are rich people who work hard,' said Vinay.

'*Rich people work hard not because of compulsion but by choice. They don't work hard because they can't pay their EMI. They work hard because they are enjoying their work, because they love their work*. Rich people do not work twelve to fourteen hours a day to make more money. It's not because they need money.

It's because they need the joy, the pleasure and the satisfaction that comes from making more money. To them money isn't the big drive; they already have plenty. The drive for them is the journey – the exhilarating feeling that comes from winning and making money.'

Mr Banerjee drank a glass of water and then continued.

'Let me get a little straight here. You do have to work hard for your money. For rich people, however, this is a temporary situation. For poor and middle-class people, it's permanent. Rich people understand that '*they*' need to work hard until their '*money*' works hard enough to take their place. They understand that the more their money works, the lesser they will have to work. They follow one simple principle: *first you work hard for your money and then let your money work harder for you.*'

Mr Banerjee then picked a sheet of blank paper and started drawing on it. While he was drawing he spoke, 'Just like any process, generating income is also a process where you feed certain inputs to get the desired output. However, the rich and poor people play this process slightly differently.' Mr Banerjee had drawn the diagram and showed it to both Ajay and Vinay.

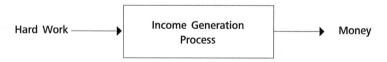

Process Flow of the Poor and Middle-Class

'This is the process flow diagram of poor and middle-class people. All throughout their life they follow this process, i.e. work hard to get money.' Mr Banerjee then handed them another sheet of diagram.

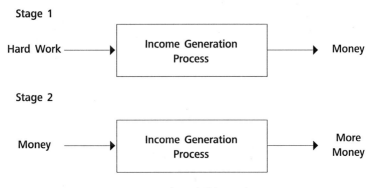

Stage 1

Hard Work ⟶ Income Generation Process ⟶ Money

Stage 2

Money ⟶ Income Generation Process ⟶ More Money

Process Flow of Rich People

'This is the process flow diagram of Rich people. First they work hard to generate income and then they let their money work hard for them. Most of the people never reach Stage 2 and hence are not able to become rich. *To become rich you need to let your money work hard for you,*' said Mr Banerjee.

'Now, based on who is working for money, i.e. whether you or your money and depending on how government treats the income earned from various source, I categorise income into four different types.

1. Active Income
2. Guaranteed Income
3. Passive Income
4. Portfolio Income

To have a healthy wallet, you need to feed your wallet with all these four incomes in right proportions. Otherwise, you will have nothing but an unhealthy wallet.'

'Sir, if you can explain in detail about these four types of income then it will be easier for us to make our wallet from unhealthy to healthy,' said Ajay who was eager to learn from the expert.

'Sure,' said Mr Banerjee. He then asked his maid to bring the white board from his kids' room which he uses to teach them maths and science lessons.

'Active income is the money earned from your active work. This includes a pay cheque from your day-to-day job. Or if you are an entrepreneur or run a business or is self-employed then it is your net profit from your business or profession. Active income requires that you are investing your own time and labour to earn money. Active income exists till the moment you give your time towards it. The moment you stop working, your active income will cease to exist. Active income is important because all things being equal the more your active income is; the more you can save and invest and which in turn will help you generate other sources of income. However there are two downsides to the active income; first being that it requires your time and energy and second that it is taxed at the highest rate of taxation.'

'So salary of all the salaried class, income earned by self-employed professionals such as doctors, lawyers, accountants etc. will come under Active income,' said Vinay.

'Correct. Now coming to guaranteed income; this income does not require you to work. Here, your money works for you. The fixed deposit that you create or a corporate bond that you purchase where there is a surety of income will come under this category. Since, the interest income here is guaranteed and certain to be received, this income again are taxed at the highest rate of taxation,' said Mr Banerjee.

Both Ajay and Vinay knew how the income tax on the

interest earned on the fixed deposit reduces its overall return and therefore they had stopped putting all their money in the fixed deposits. However, they had kept certain portion of their net worth as fixed deposits and bonds since these instruments provide liquidity and can be liquidated at the time of need.

'The third category, i.e. the passive income is the money earned without you actively working for it. Here again, your money works for you. However against the guaranteed income where there is a surety of the income, here there is no specific surety which means you do not know for sure how much you would make beforehand. The income can be more than what you expect or it can be less than your expectations. Examples of income under this category would be rental income from your leased out home; dividend income from stocks and mutual funds; franchisee income; royalties from books, music, movies or from your patented idea/product etc.'

'All the rich people have one or more sources of passive income. Take the example of KFC. Colonel Sanders, who is the founder of KFC does not go and sit in every outlet of KFC. Rather, he has developed a method of preparing fried chicken and has granted the right to every outlet owners to carry out the business of selling fried chicken to customers using his trademark. And in return, he gets a percentage of their income. So, he just sits at home and every KFC outlet owners keep on filling the wallet of Colonel Sanders which is nothing but Passive Income for him because he is not actively involved in the running of every KFC outlet across the world.'

'The beauty of Passive Income is that it keeps on generating a stream of income for you even if you are not present there. Even when you are sleeping or have gone out for vacation, the passive income keeps filling your wallet. And since there is no surety of return from the passive income, the taxman gives a lot of deductions and actual rate of tax is much lower than the tax rate applicable for active and guaranteed income. In certain cases like dividend income, there is no tax at all.'

Mr Banerjee paused for some time and allowed both Ajay and Vinay to grasp the idea. He knew that it is the passive income which helps people become rich; so he wanted both of them to think over sometime on the ideas of passive income before he proceeded.

'And what about the portfolio income?' asked Ajay after thinking about the passive income for some time.

'Well, portfolio income is the income generated when you sell off any of your assets. The benefit of owning an asset is that not only it gives you income all throughout its life when you hold that asset, in the form of passive income; it also makes money for you when you dispose of the asset. The income earned from disposing off the asset is termed as portfolio income.'

'Take the example of real estate. Suppose Vinay purchases a two bedroom apartment in Bengaluru for ₹50 lakhs. He puts this apartment on rent and earns rental income of ₹2 lakh per annum. This rental income is his passive income. To earn this income Vinay don't have to work hard. Here his money invested in the real estate is working to generate income for him. Now suppose after 5 years, due to increased demand of real estate and its limited supply, Vinay's property price has increased to ₹80 lakhs. He now thinks of realising the profit and then sells his apartment and earns a handsome profit of ₹30 lakhs. This income, which Vinay earned by selling off his asset is his portfolio income. Here again, since you don't work for money but your money invested in the form of assets bring income to you, the taxman eyes it with relative leniency and tax rate on portfolio income is lesser than that applicable for active income. In fact, many types of portfolio income are tax free such as long-term capital gain on shares and long term capital gain on real estate if you are able to meet certain conditions which is not the case with the active income.'

'Sir, what happens if the prices of our property such as shares/stocks/bonds, gold or real estate keeps on increasing and we don't sell them? Will it still account for portfolio income?' asked Vinay.

'It will account for your portfolio income, but in the form of unrealised income,' said Mr Banerjee.

'What is this unrealised income?' asked Ajay who now had a curiosity of a 3-year-old child and was eager to learn something, which nobody had taught him in 30 years.

'Unrealised income is the notional profit that you earn on holding an asset and which is yet to be cashed in. This happens when the present market value of the asset is higher than what you had initially paid for it and you are yet to sell that asset. So what happens in this case is that your wealth has appreciated but you have not encashed the profit.'

'But why would anybody not encash the profit?' asked Ajay.

'Well, there are two reasons for that. The first being the expectations the investor has for further appreciation of his asset. He/She believes that market value of his/her asset would increase further in future and that's why they hold on to it for a longer period and do not encash the unrealised profit.'

'The second and the most important reason for not encashing the unrealised income is that the moment you encash your unrealised income, you are taxed for the capital gain.[12] The government keeps a close watch on all your bank accounts. As soon as it sees that there is an inflow of cash into your account, it will tax you. And this is the reason; Rich people don't keep their money in the bank. Rather they keep it in the form of real estate, shares/stocks, bonds and businesses. All these assets bring passive and portfolio income to them. It is the middle-class who keep most of their money in their bank in the form of saving accounts and fixed deposits and are taxed heavily.'

Mr Banerjee looked at both Ajay and Vinay to see if they have any questions and then continued.

'Take our earlier example where Vinay had made the profit of ₹30 lakhs by selling his apartment. If he brings in this money in his account, he will be taxed for the capital gain of ₹30 lakhs and his overall wealth/net worth would have come down to the extent of tax paid. But if he had not sold his property then he would not have to pay tax and his overall wealth would not have decreased. *Remember, there is no tax on wealth but if you convert your wealth into income by selling off your assets and bringing in the money into your bank account then you will have to pay income tax and your overall wealth with come down.'*

'However, if Vinay reinvests the entire sale proceeds of ₹80 lakhs in another residential property then he does not need to pay any capital gain tax. Because if he does so; then there is no realisable income. Our income tax rules allow a seller to delay paying taxes in a piece of real estate that is sold for a capital gain through an exchange for a more expensive piece

---

[12]The tax rate on short-term capital gain is usually lower than the tax rate applicable for active income.

of real estate. Real estate is one investment vehicle that has a great tax advantage. *As long as you keep trading up in value, you will not be taxed on the gains until you liquidate, i.e. cash in the profit.* So, to become rich always remember this simple formula coined by the famous author, lecturer and researcher, Dr Thomas J Stanley.

To build wealth, minimise your realisable (taxable) income and maximise your unrealised income (wealth/capital appreciation without a cash flow).

For most of the upper middle-class households, Income Tax is the single largest annual expenditure. It is tax on income, not on wealth/asset and not in the appreciation of wealth if this appreciation is not realised; that is if it does not generate a cash flow.'

'If minimising our realisable income and maximising our unrealised income would increase our wealth then why do people focus so much on their realised income?' asked Vinay.

'Before I answer your question, let me first reframe your question,' said Mr Banerjee. 'It is not all people who focus on their realised income. It is only the middle-class who focus on their realised income; their bank balance. Rich people are always in their pursuit to maximise their unrealised income so that they don't have to pay tax. *Rich people measure their success with their total assets; their net worth. Middle-class measure their success with their realised income.'*

'Now coming to your question that why middle-class focus on realised income; well, there are two reasons for it. First reason is their ignorance on the subject of income tax. Second reason is that middle-class maximise their realised income only to support their high-consumption lifestyle. They cannot purchase high end branded clothes with money invested in stocks, bonds and real estate. So they sell their stocks, pay tax on the capital gain, if any and with the balance amount that has been credited to their bank account they go out for shopping.'

Mr Banerjee then stood up and drew a table on the white board which his maid had brought earlier.

Income Type	Active Income	Guaranteed Income	Passive Income	Portfolio Income
Who works for it	You	Your Money	Your Money	Your Money
Taxation rate	Highest	Highest	Low or Nil	Low or Nil
Amount of Income	Mostly Fixed and is capped to your salary or on your scale of business	Fixed	Not Fixed and there is no cap on the income	Not Fixed and there is no cap on the income

'So as you see here, for passive and portfolio income there is either very low or nil tax and that there is no cap on the income that can be generated through passive and portfolio income, i.e. passive and portfolio income is not limited by any boundary. It can reach to any level if you use your money wisely. However, if you do not put money wisely and invest in any stocks, mutual funds without doing proper study then you may make loss also. On the other hand, your active income is bounded by your salary or on the scale of your business/ profession. This is the reason why you cannot become rich with just your active income because first it is bounded, second it requires your time and energy and lastly it is taxed heavily.' Mr Banerjee then drew a graph on the white board.

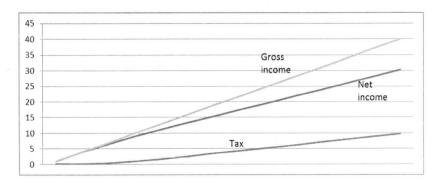

'This is the graph of active income,' said Mr Banerjee. 'As the active income increases, so does the income tax. For a person who falls under the highest tax bracket, he/she pays nearly 25% to 30% of his/her gross income as income tax. This simply means that for a person whose only source of income is active income then out of the 12-month period from January to December, he/she never gets income for the month of January to March, i.e. all the income earned from January to March goes as the income tax. To put it more simply, this person works for the government from January to March and then from April to December he/she works for him/herself.'

Both Ajay and Vinay were dumbfounded at this revelation and looked at each other in surprise. While they were paying income tax on their salary, they never had realised that though they work for 12 months; they get to keep income only for the 9 months.

'And this is the reason you are falling back one step after

you take 3 steps forward,' said Mr Banerjee looking at Vinay. 'Because whenever you earn ₹100 by your hard work – the Government will take away ₹30 from you as income tax. Always remember that increasing your active income by working hard might increase your current income by a few percentage points, it will never help you create a long term wealth unless you know how to make money work for you'

'While active income is bounded, requires your time and energy and is taxed heavily; the passive and portfolio income on the other hand is unbounded, does not require your time and energy and is taxed leniently,' continued Mr Banerjee. 'When you work for money as in the case of active income, the government takes a sizeable portion of that income. But when your money is working for you as in the case of passive and portfolio income, the Government allows you to keep the income with you.'

'*Our tax system is such that it penalises people who work hard and awards those who work smartly by letting their money work for them.* Or to put it in another way, our Government discourages you to work hard; rather it wants you to work smartly wherein you let your money work hard for you,' Mr Banerjee paused for some time and then continued. 'To help you realise the real beauty of passive and portfolio income, I show you another diagram for you because I believe a picture says more than a thousand words.' He showed them a set of diagrams that were part of a PPT. When they saw the diagram, Ajay and Vinay completely changed their perspectives about the different categories of income.

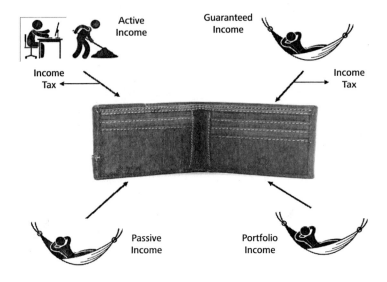

Both Ajay and Vinay looked at the diagram then at each other and then at Mr Banerjee who was standing beside the white board and was smiling. After giving them sufficient time to look at the diagram and having realised that both of his students had grasped the meaning of the diagram he continued, 'Poor people focus only on active income. Middle-class people focus on active income and try to generate some guaranteed income. And rich people focus entirely on generating passive and portfolio income while keeping their active and guaranteed income intact. Though they have income stream coming from active and guaranteed sources, their focus is mainly on the passive and portfolio income. Now since you two want to become rich, I will tell you the key.' Mr Banerjee looked at both Ajay and Vinay who were listening to him with their ears and eyes open and then continued *'the key to become rich and wealthy is to increase the proportion of your*

passive and portfolio income as quickly as possible. Without passive and portfolio income nobody can become rich. It is the passive and portfolio income which makes Mukesh Ambani the richest man in India and not his active income.'

'If passive and portfolio income is so important to become wealthy, then why don't people focus on generating passive and portfolio income?' asked Vinay.

'It is because of our conditioning,' said Mr Banerjee who now had taken his seat on the sofa set.

'What is this conditioning all about?' asked Ajay.

'It is how we have been programmed' said Mr Banerjee. 'Since our childhood days we have been taught that to need money, we need to work hard. All our teachers and in fact most of our parents teach us that we need to get good grades so that we can get a good job and then work hard in our job to earn money. All throughout our childhood days we have been bombarded with statements that if we don't work hard, we will never be able to make money. Even in our college days, we get to hear that we need to get a good job in a good company to get good money.'

'Never have we been taught that we can create passive income without working hard. And since nobody has taught us to earn passive income, we don't give it much attention even when we have started working. We largely choose our career options based on active income that it would bring to us. *If all of us would have known that our primary objective is to create passive and portfolio income, then I guess many people would reconsider their career choices.*'

'Sir now that we understand the different types of income and its tax implications and that we need to have a healthy wallet to become rich, is there any other ways in which we can reduce our overall tax?' asked Vinay.

'Use the magic of corporations,' said Mr Banerjee with a smile.

Both Ajay and Vinay looked at him with surprise. Their face clearly told that they didn't get a clue about what he had told them just now. After sensing that his words didn't do anything apart from creating a line of suspense in their head, Mr Banerjee thought of explaining it to them.

'What is the purpose of Income Tax or why does the government levy income tax on us?' asked Mr Banerjee.

'Government needs funds to run the country. It has to run the administration, maintain law and order, protect our border, provide for welfare services such as health, education and build infrastructure for the development of the country. All these require huge public finance and income tax is one of the major sources of revenue for the government,' said Ajay.

'You have put it correctly. But no one has described the system of income tax better than the most celebrated Sanskrit poet to ever live in India – *Kalidasa*. Kalidasa in his epic poem *Raghuvamsha* narrated the stories related to Raghu dynasty, namely the family of King Dilipa and his descendants. In this poem, Kalidasa says about King Dilipa *'It was only for the good of his subjects that he collected taxes from them, just as the Sun draws moisture from the Earth to give it back a thousand fold.'* So collection of income tax is essential for the government to run a country and that is the reason I am very prompt in sending notices to those people who try to evade tax.'

'If income tax is so essential for the government to run the country then shouldn't we be paying income tax completely instead of finding ways to save it?' asked Vinay.

'The government collects taxes from its citizens based on certain laws and rules. They have the legal right to collect taxes and we, Income Tax officers make sure that people pay income tax on time. However, just as the government has the right to legally collect taxes from us, all the citizen of the country have the right to save taxes in a legal way. Government has provided us with opportunities to save tax. These opportunities have been given to us as a reward for channelling our money into areas the government thinks helps the economy. And if people are not using those opportunities and saving taxes then probably they are paying more than their share of tax that the government is expecting them to pay.'

'So, how can we save tax and pay only to that extent what government expects us to pay?' asked Ajay.

'Like I said earlier; use the magic of corporations.'

'We don't know any such magic,' said Vinay smilingly.

'I guess today I will teach you some magic,' said Mr Banerjee winking his eyes. 'Income tax in India is broadly divided into two parts, namely personal income tax and corporate tax. Though there are different rates for taxation on the two, the most distinct difference between the two is the method of calculating taxable income. For an individual, income tax is computed based on his total income and the person has to pay the income tax even before he can pay for his grocery. However in the case of a corporate, it does not pay tax on its income. Rather, its income tax is computed based on its profit; that is, it pays tax on the amount that is left after meeting all its expenses.'

Mr Banerjee then got up from his seat and started drawing two tables on the white board.

Individual		Corporate	
Income	100	Income	100
Tax @30% of Income	30	Expenses	60
Expenses	60	Profit Before Tax (PBT)	40
		Tax @30% of PBT	12
Net Profit	10	Net Profit	28

'Suppose there is an individual or a corporate, both have an income of ₹100 and expense of ₹60 each. You may think that since their income and expense is same, their savings will also be same. In reality that is not the case. A corporate gets to keep around 3 times the money that an individual can keep in his wallet after meeting expenses. So, what is happening here? Is there some magic by which a corporate is able to retain more money than an individual despite both of them earning same income and having same expense? No, there is no magic. It is the difference between the methodology by which tax is computed for an individual and a corporate. *Individuals earn and get taxed and try to live with what is left. A company earns, spend everything it can and then is taxed on anything that is left.* So, if you want to save your tax, first become a company and then earn through the company.'

'But Sir, we cannot earn our salary through a company,' interrupted Vinay.

'True, a person drawing his salary cannot earn it by becoming a corporate. But, he still has other three sources of income, namely guaranteed, passive and portfolio income. And for these three sources of income he has the choice whether he wants to earn them as an Individual or by as being a Corporate.'

'How is it possible to earn guaranteed, passive and portfolio income by as being a corporate?' asked Ajay.

'You would have noticed that these three sources of income come only by owning certain assets such as fixed deposits, bonds, real estates, stocks and businesses etc. Normally, middle-class people own these assets in their name and then earn these incomes as an individual and hence pay heavy tax. Rich people on the other hand first create a company and then let his company owns the asset. And then all the guaranteed, passive and portfolio income earned is in the name of the company. This helps the Rich people reduce the tax payment,' said Mr Banerjee.

Mr Banerjee then started cleaning the white board. He spoke, 'I will draw another diagram to help you understand the structure.'

'While middle-class hold all their assets in their name and earn the income in their name again only to pay heavy tax; Rich people first create a company 'Rich Pvt. Ltd.' and then own the assets in the name of the company. So when these assets produce income, it is the income of the company rich Pvt Ltd and hence there is very less tax. However, the entire assets and the income are still being owned by the rich person; though indirectly.'

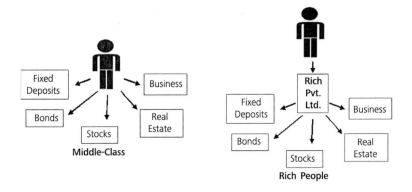

Middle-Class

Rich People

Both Ajay and Vinay were surprised to see how through a simple method, rich people are able to save tax. They were happy that they were learning the ways rich people invest their money. However, Ajay still had one more question in his mind.

'Sir, we don't have land, factories or offices of our own. And we don't have money to pay salaries to employees. Then how do we create a company?'

Mr Banerjee started laughing upon hearing Ajay's question. Ajay felt a little embarrassed; thinking that he must have asked some stupid question. However, he knew that it was better to get his doubts clarified; otherwise all this wisdom that he received today would go waste.

'This is one of the biggest misconceptions that people have in their mind. They think that they need land, factory, offices etc. to create a company and that only rich people can start a company. Nothing could be farther from truth. In today's age, a company means nothing but a legal document prepared by your chartered accountant and filed in the appropriate government office. That's all. Your company is just a legal document that creates a legal body without a soul. It's as easy to create a company as it is to buy any asset. Therefore it is in your interest to create a company for yourself and own assets through your company' said Mr Banerjee.

Now both Ajay and Vinay knew what they would do once they reach their home. They recalled their respective CAs who had helped them file their income tax returns and thought of approaching them the very next day. Both of them now knew that they have to create a wealthy wallet so that they can relax while passive and portfolio income would continue to pour streams of money in their wallet continuously. While Ajay was thinking of creating streams of passive and portfolio income for himself, Vinay was thinking of consolidating his existing passive and portfolio income so that its overall share in his total wallet increases.

Part III

THE BEGINNING

Ten

THE BUTTERFLY EFFECT

When Ajay came to meet Vinay after a fortnight, he had already created a company in his name. He also had started making investments in the name of his company with the help of his CA. He told Vinay that his CA was very pleased to know that he wanted to make his investments through creating a private limited company.

'Only rich people do the way you are making your investment. I have few HNIs who follow the same approach. It helps them to reduce their taxes – this is what my CA told me when I asked him to create a company in my name,' said Ajay.

'My CA also told the same,' said Vinay. 'I think with this approach we will be able to save a lot of tax and our net income would increase dramatically.'

'True. So, what is it for today?' asked Ajay.

'Today, there is nothing much to share with you but only

one table that I prepared yesterday when you had called me in the evening,' said Vinay. He then asked Ajay whether he knows about the butterfly effect. Ajay told that he had heard about it and that a movie has been made with the same name but is not able to recall it exactly.

'Butterfly effect is a scientific term coined by the meteorologist Edward Lorenz in which he observed that the solutions to a highly simplified weather model were sensitive to initial conditions. He tells that a very small and insignificant event can end up creating huge impacts somewhere else. It is similar to an event of a butterfly snapping its wings in the USA and the wave created out of the wing snap multiples itself over time and space develops the capacity to create a hurricane in China and hence the name butterfly effect.'

'Yes, I remember that now,' said Ajay. 'But what does it have to do with money and wealth?'

'Butterfly effect has applications everywhere. It is part of the Chaos theory which deals with nonlinear things that are effectively impossible to predict or control, like turbulence, weather, the stock market, our brain states and so on. Only thing is that it is known by different names in different fields. And when it comes to personal finance, about money and wealth then this Butterfly Effect is known as compound interest.'

'But how compound interest can cause a small and insignificant event to end up creating a big impact?' asked Ajay.

'Do you smoke?' asked Vinay.

'No,' replied Ajay.

'Do you drink?'

'No.'

'You must be going to the movies and then dinner or lunch in some restaurant?'

'Yes'

'And how much does it cost you on an average?'

'I guess we go to a movie and then dinner almost once a week. And the average cost of movie and dinner combined for two of us including fuel for the car would come to around ₹2000,' said Ajay.

'So, you mean to say that you spend almost ₹8000 every month on movies and dining out.'

'It looks like but we never realised it.'

'What if I say to you that instead of going out for movies and dinner every week, you go for it every fortnight? Will it be a big problem for you?'

'I guess, it would not be a big problem,' said Ajay.

'So when you decide to go to watch movie and dine out every alternate week instead of every week, you save nearly ₹4,000 per month. This is equivalent to saving ₹135 per day. This amount may not look big to you. People these days spend ₹135 every day on trivial items like tea, coffee and burger so it should not sound like a big deal to save ₹135 per day. But imagine you save this amount of ₹135 every day and deposit it in some retirement plan. Assuming your retirement plan gives you a return of 10% per annum, what would be the amount that you would receive once you retire at the age of 65? Remember, you are just saving ₹135 every day and putting in your retirement account.'

Ajay tried to calculate the figure in his mind. He thought ₹4,000 multiplied by 12 comes to around ₹48,000, which is the amount he would save in a year. Now he is 30 years of age. So, he would be saving this amount for 35 years. ₹48,000 multiplied by 35 would be around ₹17 lakhs. And he would be earning interest on the amount also. 'I guess, it would amount to some ₹24–25 lakhs,' said Ajay.

Vinay shook his head.

'I guess ₹30 lakhs.'

'Try again,' said Vinay.

'It can't be more than ₹35 lakhs. After all, I saved only ₹17 lakhs throughout the period. How it can be more than double the amount that I saved.'

Vinay then took out his laptop. He filled in the numbers in the excel sheet. And when he was done with his calculations, he spoke, 'Your daily savings of ₹135 would give you a whopping amount of nearly ₹1.50 crores.'

'What!' exclaimed Ajay. He was staring at Vinay, his eyes wide. 'I don't believe this.'

'Look for yourself,' Vinay turned his laptop towards Ajay.

Ajay went through the number that Vinay had punched in the excel sheet. When he saw the final amount, he was completely taken back.

'So, you mean to say that by saving only ₹135 per day, I would be making an amount of ₹1.50 crores once I retire at the age of sixty-five.'

'That I am not saying. It is the mathematics, which is telling it. That's what the excel sheet has calculated. I just put in the numbers,' said Vinay with a smile.

Ajay was still not convinced. He went through the numbers and tried to find out the amount by himself. And again, he got the same amount.

'So, *my movies and dining out is costing me ₹1.50 crores.* I never realised it that way.'

'That is the butterfly effect for you. And that is the magic of compound interest. What you are doing is that you are simply taking out ₹135 from your wallet and putting it in your retirement account. And once you reach the age of 65; when you plan to hang up your boots and check your retirement account; you would notice that yours daily collection of a small amount; the amount which is as small as ₹135 has turned itself into a giant of ₹1.50 crores.'

'By saving ₹135 per day, you were doing nothing but just snapping a wing of butterfly everyday and with the passage of time; those snaps have resulted into a hurricane. Only thing is that this hurricane does not do any harm to you; rather it helps you at the time when you need the money most so that you can have a very comfortable life post retirement,' said Vinay.

'But what will be the worth of ₹1.50 crores 35 years down the line? Will not inflation decrease it value?' asked Ajay.

'Inflation is going to have an impact. But it will not be a devastating one. In fact, inflation is all the more reason to save. Things are going to be more expensive as the time progresses. Your food items are going to be costly. The fuel that you need be it LPG, petrol or diesel – everything is going to cost you more 35 years from now. And that is why I ask you to save now so that you would be able to afford these items when they become very costly. *Actually, it is the person who doesn't save in his productive years who has to worry about inflation and not the person who does.*'

'But for that, I need to forgo the fun and entertainment that we would otherwise have at the time when we are young,' said Ajay a little sceptic.

'Before I answer your question, let me tell you a story. There was a guy called David. By chance or by luck, he discovers a gold mine near his house. While he was trying to study the soil and its texture, he called out his younger brother Will:

'Hey Will, I have got this gold mine at the backyard of our house. It's so much gold and I don't know what to do with it all. Come over here and help me dig.'

Will says: 'But I don't have a shovel. How will I dig?'

'Well Will, go out and get one.'

After a while, Will returns and says 'Do you know what they are asking for shovels these days?'

The point I am trying to say here is that *if you want to get a gold mine for yourself then you should not worry about the price of the shovel.'*

Ajay realised what Vinay was trying to convey to him. He understood that by forgoing some fun by saving a small amount of ₹135 per day, he can create a fortune for himself.

'See, everyone of us wastes money on a daily basis on items such as fancy coffee, bottled water, packed sandwiches and burgers, cigarettes, soft drinks, candy bars, fast food. The list can go on and on. We all throw away too much of our hard-earned money on unnecessary little expenses without realising how much they can add up to. So if you cut down your unnecessary expenses and are able to save ₹135 everyday and keep it in your retirement account then you are helping yourself only. You are creating a better and brighter future for yourself and your family. And all this happens just at the cost of ₹135 per day.'

'I am not telling you to squirrel away every rupee and every paise of yours. But, if you want to accomplish your goals, you must save something. Remember by cutting down your daily expense by ₹135, you do not downgrade your lifestyle. Neither you become too much of a miser, who doesn't enjoy his life. I am sure; you can have all the fun and still save ₹135 per day.'

Ajay had no words to say now. He was feeling guilty but at the same time was feeling enlightened to have received the wisdom of butterfly effect on personal finance.

'You would have met many people who say that saving and investment should be done only when you plan to retire; that the young age is the time when you should enjoy the most. These people would be the one who would spend their entire salary in the first four–five years of their professional career. And once they start saving and making investments, they feel that they are not able to save. They don't realise that if they were not able to save when they were young, when their liabilities were less, then how they can save when they have kids to take care of, including their school and college fees and when their parents become old and their medical expenses have risen dramatically.'

'To these people, I just want to show one table. This table beautifully captures the power of compounding interest. This table has the butterfly effect in action.'

Vinay then got up and brought the table which he had prepared last evening. When he presented the table to Ajay, he was just observing Ajay's face. Ajay was first surprised and then he looked tensed and then was suddenly smiling.

'This table has changed my entire perspective on money. And I am sure; it would change anybody's idea about money. Compound Interest is really a powerful tool,' said Ajay.

'That's what Albert Einstein has said about Compound Interest. He said, *"Compound Interest is the eighth wonder of the world. He, who understands it, earns it; he who doesn't, pays it."*'

All three: Vijay, Rahul and Prem invest in similar investment tools, which give a return of 10% per annum								
Vijay starts investing at the age of 26 for next 5 years. After that he stops investing.			Rahul starts investing at the age of 31 for next 8 years. After that he stops investing.			Prem starts investing at the age of 39 for next 27 years, i.e. till his retirement		
Age	Invest ₹	Value ₹	Age	Invest ₹	Value ₹	Age	Invest ₹	Value ₹
26	60000	66000	26			26		
27	60000	138600	27			27		
28	60000	218460	28			28		
29	60000	306306	29			29		
30	60000	402937	30			30		
31		443230	31	60000	66000	31		
32		487553	32	60000	138600	32		
33		536309	33	60000	218460	33		
34		589939	34	60000	306306	34		
35		648933	35	60000	402937	35		
36		713827	36	60000	509230	36		
37		785209	37	60000	626153	37		
38		863730	38	60000	754769	38		
39		950103	39		830245	39	60000	66000
40		1045114	40		913270	40	60000	138600
41		1149625	41		1004597	41	60000	218460
42		1264588	42		1105057	42	60000	306306
43		1391046	43		1215562	43	60000	402937
44		1530151	44		1337119	44	60000	509230
45		1683166	45		1470831	45	60000	626153
46		1851483	46		1617914	46	60000	754769
47		2036631	47		1779705	47	60000	896245
48		2240294	48		1957675	48	60000	1051870
49		2464324	49		2153443	49	60000	1223057
50		2710756	50		2368787	50	60000	1411363

51		2981832	51		2605666	51	60000	1618499
52		3280015	52		2866233	52	60000	1846349
53		3608016	53		3152856	53	60000	2096984
54		3968818	54		3468141	54	60000	2372682
55		4365700	55		3814956	55	60000	2675950
56		4802270	56		4196451	56	60000	3009545
57		5282496	57		4616096	57	60000	3376500
58		5810746	58		5077706	58	60000	3780150
59		6391821	59		5585476	59	60000	4224165
60		7031003	60		6144024	60	60000	4712581
61		7734103	61		6758426	61	60000	5249840
62		8507513	62		7434269	62	60000	5840824
63		9358265	63		8177696	63	60000	6490906
64		10294091	64		8995466	64	60000	7205997
65		11323500	65		9895012	65	60000	7992596
Total amount invested: ₹3,00,000 Vijay's earning beyond investment: ₹1,10,23,500			Total amount invested: ₹4,80,000 Rahul's earning beyond investment: ₹94,15,012			Total amount invested: ₹16,20,000 Prem's earning beyond investment: ₹63,72,596		

Ajay was about to give the table back to Vinay but then had a relook at it to appreciate and grasp its beauty.

After Ajay returned the table to Vinay, Vinay spoke: 'It all depends on you. Whether you want to be Vijay who just saves for 5 years at the beginning of his career or you want to be like Prem who saves for 27 years of his working life and still end up getting less than Vijay. If you are able to appreciate the power of compound interest and the Butterfly Effect in action in wealth creation and accumulation and apply it in your real life then you will never struggle financially.'

'Remember, just like Butterfly Effect takes time to show its real power, Compound Interest also shows its magic when you give it sufficient time. And that is why the sooner a person starts saving, the better he would be off. Because, when a person starts early then even if his monthly savings may be small, the time will more than compensate for his small savings.'

'If you show this table to someone who says that 'I don't like saving because I want to enjoy my life,' he would say but how come I would be able to save ₹5,000 every month. To him, my reply would be: whether they really want to have fun for five years or they would like to have fun for thirty-five years. Because, if they want to have fun for thirty-five years then they need to be a little disciplined in their early five years and try to save as small as ₹5,000 every month. And yes, by saving ₹5,000 every month, nobody becomes a loser who doesn't enjoy his/her life.'

'I understand that to unleash the power of compound interest, I need to start saving as early as possible. But why did you ask me if I smoke and drink?' asked Ajay.

'If you would have told that you smoke and/or drink then

I would have asked you to cut down the number of your cigarettes and drinks so that instead of saving ₹135 you save a minimum of ₹250 daily.'

On hearing Vinay's reply, Ajay started laughing and then Vinay also joined him.

Eleven

BIRDS OF A FEATHER FLOCK TOGETHER

'Now that we are close to the end of our journey, there is one last point that I thought I should tell you,' said Vinay taking a bite of muffin.

The two friends were meeting after a gap of nearly six months in a cafe near Vinay's new house. He had sold his old two bedroom flat and had moved to a three bedroom apartment in a residential society.

During this period, Ajay saw his wealth increasing slowly and steadily. He was checking his net worth every two months and was pleased to see its growth. He was happy that he had started investing in Good Assets through his newly formed company which brings passive and portfolio income to him. Though he felt guilty sometimes that he had not started his journey of financial freedom earlier but was happy that he started it as soon as he got to know the power of butterfly effect. He thought that he still has ample time left to get the benefit of compound interest; the eighth wonder of the world. And yes, he was happy that he had started paying himself first and was on the way to be free – free from all the financial burdens.

'Tell me. I am all eager to learn from you,' said Ajay taking a sip from his cup of coffee.

'Have you ever seen a luxury car you wanted, drive by and park close to where you have parked your own car? When the person gets out of the car, you feel a little resentment towards that person? Has that ever happened to you?' asked Vinay.

'Yes, sometimes it has happened to me.'

'Now that you are married but suppose five-six years ago when you were single, you saw a beautiful woman in a restaurant sitting alone and right before you make your move, her husband or boyfriend walks up and sits down and the same thing happens, you hate that guy as he has what you want– the girl. Has it happened to you?'

'Yes, many a times,' replied Ajay to which both started laughing.

'Lucky bastard! That's what we used to call them. Isn't it?

'Yes.' Ajay replied with a smile.

'Ok. Now tell me, who is your role model? Whom do you look up to?' asked Vinay.

'Well, I am inspired greatly by Steve Jobs. His life is an inspiration for everyone. One day, I also want to become like him. I too want to develop some world class product.'

'So, you want to become like Steve Jobs. Good. Now, tell me

do you like Steve Jobs or do you hate him and resent his success?'

'Why on Earth would I hate him? Rather, I look up to him and admire his hard work and the success he has achieved.'

'Good. Most people admire their role model just like you do. But when it comes to admiring rich people, they have a different perspective. Most of the poor and middle-class people do not appreciate the wealth and success of rich people. And if someone in their known circle; be it relatives, friends or office colleagues has achieved success and created wealth for himself then instead of admiring or appreciating their effort, they would resent and envy their success. They would be jealous of their wealth and say that they're lucky. Or if someone rich just goes past them in some classy car, they would whisper under their breath – these rich jerks.'

'Yes. That has happened with me also,' said Ajay.

'Everyone wants to become wealthy and successful and yet detest and hate people who are wealthy and successful. You must understand that *if you view rich people as bad in any way and if you want to be a good person then you can never become rich. It's impossible because your views and your desires are contradictory in nature.* How can you be something you despise? It pains me when someone says that they want to become rich and at the same time say that rich people are bad and evil.'

'But aren't all the rich bad and greedy? The way it is shown in movies and TVs,' said Ajay.

'Well, that is an altogether different game plan of the movie producers and directors.' Vinay then explained how producers and directors depict poor and middle-class person as good guy and rich people as bad and evil in order to gain empathies and support of a thousand people at the cost of ten people. He told what his father had told him when he had went home after his campus placement, that for every ten rich people, there are thousands poor and middle-class people. And since producers and directors want to earn as much money as possible, they depict the larger section of the society as good people.

'TV and our media also play its part to depict rich people as bad and evil,' said Vinay.

'How?'

'It is a known fact that around 70% of our population lives in rural areas where most of the people are poor or at the best middle-class. And it is also well known that number of crimes in rural areas are almost at the same level if not more than that in urban India, be it murder, rape, honour killing, ransom, loot etc. But the media houses will never cover these crimes in as detailed way as they cover a crime committed by a rich person in a city. Take for example any case, where a high profile person is accused of killing someone. All of a sudden this killing will become a national issue – it will continue to run 24...or at least ten days in all news channels as breaking news.'

'Why do our media and TV channels take so much pleasure in reporting a rich person as criminal, even though the crime charges labelled against him has not been proven by the Court? It is because all of us, who are mostly poor and middle-class people like to see rich people as bad and evil. All of us like to see them go to jail even if they have not committed any crime, because in our mind we believe that they have committed a crime by becoming rich. They have taken away all our money and wealth from us and that is why there is no money left for us to become rich and to enjoy luxuries of life.'

'But, isn't it true that wealth is limited and if it is stacked by the rich people then there will be hardly any money left for the middle-class and poor people?'

Vinay then explained to Ajay that wealth is not limited; rather it is unlimited. It is produced whenever someone undertakes an economic activity and exerts energy in a productive way.

'If the total money and wealth is limited, then how come GDP of our country or for that matter any country is increasing every year? It is because; every year people of our country are producing something or are rendering services which then creates money and wealth. So, the fact that the money and wealth is limited and that rich people have amassed all the wealth and because of which poor and middle-class people have nothing left for them is completely false – bogus.'

'Remember, most of the rich people have created the wealth by following the rules of wealth creation and accumulation. They have worked diligently and with persistence, perseverance and their desire to become rich, they have taken the necessary actions to create wealth for themselves. Poor and middle-class are not aware of the rules of wealth creation and accumulation. When their so-called hard work doesn't yield the desired result, they start blaming rich people of amassing all the wealth, which has led them to remain poor. They play a perfect victim passing on the blame to others, because it is always easy to blame someone rather than take action to improve one's lifestyle.'

'I am not saying all the rich people are good. Just like there are good and bad people in poor and middle-class families, there are good and bad people in rich families as well. Goodness and/ or badness have nothing to do with money.'

'Most of the people have been conditioned to believe that

you can't be rich and a good person or rich and spiritual. I too used to think this way. Like many of us, I was told by friends, teachers, media and the rest of the society that rich people are somehow bad, that they were all greedy, until my father opened my eyes. And since then, I have realised from my personal experience that richest people I know are also the nicest. They are also the most generous. Not to say that people who aren't rich aren't nice and generous. But I can safely say the idea that all rich people are somehow bad is nothing more than ignorance.'

'Listen and I want you to remember this forever: Not all rich people are evil. But it is people's habit of hating and resenting rich people which is evil; because hating and resenting someone does no good to anyone. When you hate rich people you do not actually hate them; you hate the money that they have created and accumulated. And if you hate money then money will never come to you. How can something come to you if you hate them?'

'Why do I say that people actually don't hate rich people but they hate the money that they have made. It is because the moment that rich person become poor because of some ill fate then suddenly all the hatred of the people turns into love and sympathies for him. So, in reality they never hated that person, but his money. Once their money is gone, that rich person who was earlier a bad person suddenly becomes a loveable and friendlier person.'

Ajay nodded in agreement with Vinay. He realised that there is no point in criticising rich people. He also understood that hating or resenting someone does no good to anyone. Rather, it makes him farther from his goal of creating and accumulating wealth for himself and his family.

'So what shall we do, if we do not hate and resent rich people?' asked Ajay.

'Instead of resenting rich people, I want you to practice *admiring* rich people, I want you to practice *blessing* rich people and I want you to practice *loving* rich people. That way, unconsciously you know that when you become rich, other people will admire you, bless you and love you instead of resent the heck out of you the way you might do them now.'

'If you hate Steve Jobs then I am 100% sure, that you can never become like him. Yet if you love him and admire him then there is a possibility of you becoming like him.'

'In Huna Philosophy,[13] which is better known as Hawaiian spiritualism, it is understood that when you see something you want, bless it and bless that person who has it. If you see a person with a beautiful home, bless that person and bless that home. If you see a person with a beautiful car, bless that person and bless that car. If you see a person with a loving family, bless that person and bless that family. And, if it is the beautiful woman you want, bless her beauty and bless the man beside her.'

'The more jealousy and resentment you have toward the things you desire, the less likely it is that you will have those things. It all plays a role in how your subconscious views those things. If your mind relates those negative emotions in connection with the things you want, it will steer clear and away from you.'

---

[13] *Bless that which you want.* – Huna Philosophy published by David Allred. (http://www.createfinancialwealth.com/bless-that-which-you-want-huna-philosophy/)

The Power of Association

'Now that you know how admiring, loving and blessing rich people help you in creating and accumulating wealth for you; there is one more thing which will help you a lot. It is through associating with rich people rather than staying away from them. Rich people always associate with rich and successful people. On the other hand, poor and middle-class people always tend to associate with people who are just as broke as they are.'

'But how associating with rich people will help me in becoming rich?' asked Ajay.

'You are a father now and you take great care of your daughter. Would you ever like that Kiara, once she grows up, say when she becomes a teenager, spends her time with kids who are not cultured or are in the habit of smoking, drinking or even worse are in the habit of taking drugs?'

'No, I never would allow her to fall into such a company.'

'Why?' asked Vinay.

'Because she will get all the bad habits of those spoiled kids and I definitely don't want her to be like that. I want her to grow up to a well cultured and responsible girl,' said Ajay.

'Exactly! And that is why I say that if you want to become like rich people, you better start spending time with them. When you start associating with them; you will learn from them how they became rich and successful. You will learn their thinking process, their habit and most of all, you will get access to the vast treasure of wisdom that they have learnt during their journey to be rich and successful.'

'The fastest and easiest way to create wealth is to learn exactly how rich people, who are masters of money, play the game. The goal is to simply model their inner and outer strategies. It just makes sense: if you take the exact same actions and have the exact same mind-set, chances are good that you will get the exact same results. How can you do this? It is by associating with them, going to party with them and spending time with them.'

'Remember the old Hindi Proverb that our parents have taught us since we were small – *Sangat se gun hota hai, sangat se gun jaye: bans phans aur mishri, aikai bhav bikaye* (because of the company, we earn virtues and lose virtues: as the bamboo basket containing sweets is weighed and priced as the sweets).'

'The influence of those around us is so powerful, so subtle and so gradual that often we don't realise how it can affect us. If you are around people who spend all their income, chances are excellent that you will become a spendthrift. If you're around people who go to pubs more often than movies, you're likely to join them. Such is the power of peer pressure.'

'People are like a chameleon in that they take on the attitude, behaviours, values and beliefs of the people with whom they associate most of the time. If you want to be a successful person, associate with positive people. Associate with people who are optimistic and happy – who have goals, who are moving forward in their lives. At the same time, get away from negative, critical or complaining people.'

'I come from a middle-class family; don't have friends who are very rich and wealthy. And if I go to some rich person who is unknown to me, then they would not like to spend time with me. How do I then associate with rich people?'

'You'll have to plot and scheme to do that. You don't need to do anything illegal like crashing the wedding of some rich person and joining some rich people party without invitation. But there are ways in which you can associate with rich people in a perfectly legal and civic way. You can go to concerts where rich people go. You can volunteer in some social activity in which rich people are already involved. You can go to some business promotion events or workshops and seminars conducted by personality development coaches where you will find all the rich people gathered to learn new ways to improve themselves. And once you meet them: observe them, talk with them, exchange contacts with them and if possible befriend them. Who knows you will be invited to play tennis or golf with some of the city's most influential people. You see, it's not hard to create associations.'

'Do you know why rich people join country club?' asked Vinay.

'To play golf and to spend time in their leisure,' said Ajay.

'The rich people don't just join the country club to play golf; they join to connect with other rich and successful people. There's another saying that goes '*It's not what you know, it's who you know.*' They know that by associating with other rich and successful people, they can get to learn something new. Remember, rich people are continuous learners; they are students all throughout their life. And they also give importance to the person from whom they are learning. In short, '*If you want to fly with the eagles, don't swim with the ducks!*'

'As the old saying goes –'Birds of a feather flock together.' Rich people hang around with winners and poor people hang around with losers. Why? It's a matter of comfort. Rich people are comfortable with other successful people. They feel fully worthy of being with them. Poor people are uncomfortable with highly successful people. They're either afraid that they'll be rejected or feel as if they don't belong. If you want to become rich, you need to believe that you are as worthy as them to enjoy all the luxuries of life. You need to say it to yourself that 'If they can do it, I can do it too.' And the best part is that rich people have already created a path to become rich. You just need to associate with them, learn from them and follow on the path.'

'And yes, there is another way of associating and learning with rich people,' continued Vinay. 'Find some rich and successful person and take him or her out to dinner. A poor person – and we're all poor compared to someone, no matter how well we're doing – should invest in feeding a rich person. And then do what? Just ask them and then listen what he has to say about his journey of making money. Keep on ordering starters, main course, desserts and continue the conversation as long as you can. If you get someone like this to talk with you for two hours, you can learn enough strategies and attitudes to multiply your income and change your life. But then you may say that poor people don't take rich people out to dinner. Then I would say that's probably why they are poor.'

'Azim Premji has rightly said: "If you are always in the company of cynics, you will soon find yourself becoming like them. A cynic knows all the reasons why something cannot be done. Instead, spend time with people who have a 'can-do' approach. Choose your advisors and mentors correctly. Pessimism is contagious, but then so is enthusiasm. In fact, reasonable optimism can be an amazing force multiplier."'

Meanwhile, the waiter had brought the bill to them. After paying the bills, both of them got up and started back to their home.

Twelve

THE RICHEST ENGINEER

Ajay received a call from Vinay nearly a month after their last meeting. He was busy in a meeting with his office team and skipped his call. Once he came out of the meeting room, he called back Vinay.

'Hey, are you free tomorrow evening?' asked Vinay.

'Why? What happened?'

'Mr Ajit Dewanji; the founder and chairman of Dewanji Foundation is coming to our office to deliver a speech on Philanthropy. He is on a drive to collect funds to open a school in the outskirts of Bengaluru.'

'Great. I had always wanted to listen to him. I will definitely come.'

Ajit Dewanji was born to a family originally hailing from Gujarat. His father was a noted businessman and a respected person in the trading and business fraternity. Ajit after completing his Electrical Engineering degree from USA had come back to India to join his family's business. Earlier his company was mainly into the business of cooking oil and toiletries. However, in the 1980s the young entrepreneur, recognising the importance of the emerging IT field, took advantage of the vacuum left behind by the expulsion of an MNC IT company from India by manufacturing minicomputers under technological collaboration with an American company. Thereafter Dewanji made a focused shift from soaps to software and led his company to become one of the largest IT companies in the country.

In early 2000s, Mr Dewanji founded the Dewanji Foundation, a non-profit organisation with a vision to provide quality education to all the sections of society. Mr Dewanji has been credited with some of the biggest donations the country has ever seen towards improvement of school education in India. He also had set aside more than half of his wealth towards charity to fund his philanthropy initiatives.

Ajay had obtained a visitor pass from Vinay and was sitting alongside with him in Vinay's office conference hall which was tight packed. All were eager to listen to Mr Ajit Dewanji. After MD of Vinay's company delivered a welcome speech in honour of Mr Dewanji, the stage was left for him to address the audience.

Dear Friends,

I am very happy to be with you. It is always wonderful to be with young people who are so much full of energy and ideas.

Before I begin, I want to tell you that I have come here for a purpose. As you would know that The

Dewanji Foundation is planning to set up a school for the underprivileged students of our society. It is for this purpose I have come to seek help from you all.

While making money for ourselves and our family should be one of the primary goals, restricting our lives to just making money will not bring us peace and prosperity. The real goal of our life should be to touch and improve the lives of others. And to do that, first we need to make money for ourselves and then help others. And that is why I stress on the importance of making money but again making money should not be the end.

Let me tell you from my personal experience that there is more joy in giving and seeing the smile that appears on the face of someone than sipping a cup of coffee in an luxury cafe. I was reading an article sometime back which discussed about an 11-year-old boy who wanted to buy a bicycle. This boy was standing outside the police station of the District of Columbia. The District of Columbia police auctioned off about 100 unclaimed bicycles every month. So when the auction started and the bidding opened for the first bicycle, the boy shouted 'One dollar.' The bidding however went much higher. 'One dollar,' the boy repeated hopefully each time another bicycle came up.

The auctioneer, who had been auctioning stolen or lost bikes for last forty years, noticed that the boy's hopes seemed to soar higher whenever a racer-type bicycle was put up.

Then there was just one racer left. The bidding went to eight dollars. 'Sold to that boy over there for nine dollars!' said the auctioneer. He took eight dollars from his own pocket and asked the boy for his dollar. The youngster *immediately gave his dollar, took his bicycle and started to leave. However, he went only a few feet. Carefully parking his new possession, he went back, gratefully threw his arms around the auctioneer's neck and cried.*

The auctioneer too cried because the sense of happiness and completeness that he felt that day, he had never felt it before. He had touched the life of this little boy with just mere eight dollars and the satisfaction that he received was immeasurable.

Most of us waste our money on things we think could buy happiness for us until we realise that the only way to buy happiness is to give happiness. So whatever path you take in your lives, you must always find time to give something back to someone, to your community, to your state or to your country. Reaching out and helping people will bring you more satisfaction than anything else you have ever done.

I would like to share the story of Andrew Carnegie with you. He was an American Industrialist who led the enormous expansion of the American Steel Industry in the late 19th century. At one time, he was the richest man in the world. But what did he do with his money. He gave away his money. After retiring in 1901 at the age of 66 as the world's richest man – the steel tycoon and one of the biggest industrialists that the world has ever seen; Andrew Carnegie became a philanthropist, a person who gives money to good causes. He believed in the 'Gospel of Wealth' which meant that wealthy people are morally obligated to give their money back to others in society. During the last 18 years of his life, Carnegie gave away to charities, *foundations and universities about $350 million – in 2011 it was equivalent to around ₹15 lakh crores – which was almost 90% of his fortune.*

When Andrew Carnegie had died, his desk drawer was opened. Inside one of the drawers was a yellowed sheet of paper. On that slip of paper, dated from the time he was in his twenties, Carnegie had written the main goal of his life: 'I am going to spend the first half of my life accumulating money. I am going to spend the last half of my life giving it all away.'

Today, he is better known as the biggest philanthropist that the world has ever had than as an industrialist. Why did he give away almost 90% of his fortune? It is because he knew that he had to touch as many lives as he can to derive real happiness – it lies in seeing people grow along with you. He believed that if God has given him the talent to create and accumulate wealth then it is his duty to see that all his countrymen are benefited from his talent. Remember, a talent when not shared is a talent wasted.

We all are working in a technological space and this technology has touched and changed the lives of many people. But there are many more people who are still unaware of the technology and the progress that the world is making. While to almost all of us, our country has changed a lot with improvement in infrastructure, health and education sector and definitely in the way the things are being done with the help of technology, to many of our people, our country is still the same as it was when it was freed from the British. They still believe that if you need to go to school from home then you need to hire a bullock cart. They have never heard of rapid transportation system and the metro train.

With the inventions that we see in our lives, life for us has steadily gotten better. But these inventions are not at all impacting the lives of millions of people in our country. And that is why I want to give my wealth back to the society in a way that has the most impact on the lives of our people so that they also start dreaming about the lives that we live, so that they also start sending their children to schools and colleges and so that they are also able to create a window for themselves to enter into a progressive world which is always eager to accept them with its open arms.

It is in this endeavour that I reach out to you to contribute for the cause. Remember, happiness is achieved by both receiving and giving, reaping and bestowing. It's being able to feast on harmony as well as food, on ideas as well as bread. Happiness is a life well-lived and filled with people of substance. It's a wide variety of experiences and memories that become priceless forms of currency to spend and to invest. The ultimate sense of happiness comes when you realise that you have been of help to someone in need. So, let's do our bit to make this world a better and happier place to live, as serving Humanity is the essence of life.

To end my speech, I would like to quote William A Ward: 'Before you speak, listen. Before you write, think. Before you spend, earn. Before you invest, investigate. Before you criticise, wait. Before you pray, forgive. Before you quit, try. Before you retire, save. And before you die, give.

Thank You!

The conference hall was immediately drowned into the

deafening noise of claps. The applause in the honour of Mr Dewanji continued for two minutes. The audience was full of praise for Mr Dewanji and many went ahead and shook hands with him.

While Vinay was sitting with Ajay he spoke, 'You know all the wisdom and principles that we learnt about wealth creation and accumulation, Mr Dewanji has followed each and every one of them since the beginning of his career. And that is why he has become so wealthy and is now focussing entirely on improving the lives of the marginalised sections of our society. He is truly a hero and I am sure if we follow all the wisdom and principles that we have learnt, we too will become a hero just like him.'

Vinay then got up and started moving towards the stage.

'Where are you going?' asked Ajay.

'I am going to meet **The Richest Engineer** of our country. Aren't you coming?'

FINAL THOUGHTS

Thank you for spending your precious time to read this book. After having read the book, I hope you have gained the same wisdom that Ajay learnt during his journey, the same wisdom which Vinay has utilised to be on the path of his freedom and the same wisdom, which has helped Ajit Dewanji to become The Richest Engineer of India.

Wisdom and knowledge is of no use until it is put into action. It is like you went to learn the art of wielding sword and riding horse for the war and after you have learnt all its intricacies, you say no to going to war because you are afraid of falling in the battlefield. Learning and talking about wisdom and principles is of no use. *In real world, you have to take real action to succeed.* But why do we hesitate to take action. There are primarily two reasons which forces people to stay away from taking actions: *Fear and Getting out of your Comfort Zone.* Let us spend a few minutes in discussing these internal hurdles.

Fear, doubt and worry are among the greatest obstacles not only to success, but to happiness as well. And the fear of losing money is so real that it can even make the strongest athlete to become a cripple. Remember, the fear of failure is so strong that nobody can get rid of it. I reiterate, no one in this world can say that he doesn't have any fear. Note that it is not the failure itself. Failure makes you stronger and more resilient and more determined. It is the fear of failure or the anticipation of failure that can paralyse your thoughts and your activities and hold you back from even trying to do the things that you need to do to be a big success.

However, we should also understand that fear is not at all bad. Fear is an essential part of our survival and existence. It is fear which stops a man from going near a lion and it is the fear which stops a man from jumping from a skyscraper. Fear is nothing but a necessary evil.

So, how do we overcome the fear? It is by taking the actions which our fear is stopping us to do. If you fear public speaking, then the only way to overcome this fear is go out and deliver a speech. If you are afraid of making decisions then only way to overcome this fear is to go out, think wisely and take decision quickly and stick to it. Make a habit throughout your life of doing the things you fear. *If you do the thing you fear, the death of fear is certain.*

Susan Jeffers has written a wonderful book titled, *Feel the Fear and Do It Anyway.* In this book, she has told that the biggest mistake most people make is waiting for the feeling of fear to subside or disappear before they are willing to act. These people usually wait forever because they do not know that the feeling of fear will never go away until you take action.

It is imperative to realise that it is not necessary to try to get rid of fear in order to succeed. Rich and successful people have fear, they have doubts and they have worries. But they just don't let these feelings stop them. They are willing to act in spite of fear. Poor people let fear stop them. Remember feeling of fear will always be there, it will always stop you from taking actions. But it all depends on you that what you want to become. Either you become a person who will be stopped or you become a person who can't be stopped. The choice is yours. If you want to create wealth or any kind of success, you have to be a warrior. You have to be willing to do whatever it takes. You have to train yourself to not to be stopped by anything.

However, because of ignorance and the fear of unknown most of the people play safe. They are so afraid of losing that eventually they lose. For them the pain and fear of losing money is far greater than the joy of being rich and that is why they never take actions. But you are no more ignorant. You have all the wisdom that is there in the heads of all the rich people. All you need is to take action. And whenever the feeling of fear stops you from taking the action, then I would suggest you to take a deep breath, feel the fear and do it anyway.

The difference between rich and poor people is that rich people make a habit of doing the things that poor do not like to do. And what are those things? The things that poor don't like to do are the same things that rich people don't like to do either. Yet rich and successful people do them anyway because they realise that this is the price they must pay for the success and wealth they desire.

Now, coming to the second point, which stops people from taking action – getting out of their comfort zone – why is taking action in spite of discomfort so important? It is because 'comfortable' is where you're at now. If you want to move to a new level in your life, you must break through your comfort zone and practice doing things that are not comfortable.

Poor people and most of the middle-class are not willing to be uncomfortable. Remember, being comfortable is their biggest priority in life. But let me tell you, being comfortable may make you feel warm, fuzzy and secure, but it doesn't allow you to grow. To grow as a person you have to expand your comfort zone. The only time you can actually grow is when you are outside your comfort zone.

Let me give you a simple example. Suppose you are new to swimming and you go to a trainer who teaches you to swim. When you take the first plunge into the swimming pool and your trainer asks you walk across the pool without any support, will it be a comfortable experience or an uncomfortable experience? Usually it will be uncomfortable. But what will happen afterward? The more you practice, the more comfortable it will become. And very soon, you will be swimming just like a fish and you will become as comfortable in water as you are on land. But to become comfortable in water, what you had to do. You had to come out of your comfort zone.

Everything is uncomfortable at the beginning, but if you stick with it and continue, you will eventually move through the uncomfortable zone and succeed. Then you will have a new and expanded comfort zone, which means you will have become a 'bigger' person. Again, the only time you are actually growing is when you are uncomfortable. So, if you really want to become rich and successful, you better start getting comfortable with being uncomfortable. By expanding your comfort zone, you will expand the size of your income and wealth zone.

Harv Eker has put it very beautifully. He says: 'If your goal in life is to be comfortable, I guarantee two things. First, you will never be rich. Second, you will never be happy. Happiness doesn't come from living a lukewarm life, always wondering what could have been. Happiness comes as a result of being in our natural state of growth and living up to our fullest potential.'

So, if you want to become rich and successful then you need to come out of your comfort zone and take actions. You can't climb the ladder of success with your hands in the pocket. You have to take your hands out and you need to take actions. And the actions to be taken from your side are nothing but very simple and easily doable. None of the wisdom and principles that we discussed requires you to go through a long and boring book in finance and accounting. It is all about changing your thought process and your daily habits with regard to money. I would like to reiterate the following major steps that you should follow which will help you in becoming what you have always wanted to be – free as a bird.

* Commit yourself to become rich
* Set your wealth sketch to success

    ✓ Start believing that you drive your destiny and nobody else
    ✓ Start focussing on opportunities rather than on obstacles
    ✓ Be a continuous learner all throughout your life

* Know and understand your books
* Pay yourself first (probably the most powerful step in becoming rich)
* Create a great offence and build a strong defence for yourself
* Understand the difference between the good, the bad and

the ugly assets and start investing in good assets as much as you can
- Focus on your net worth and not on your income/salary

Keep your wallet healthy by earning from the right source of income. Focus on generating Passive and Portfolio Income:

- Learn to use the power of corporations
- Use the magic of eighth wonder of the world – compound interest. The butterfly effect will help you.
- Start praising and admiring all the rich and successful people. And start spending time with them.
- Finally, give it back to the society

Before I conclude, I would like to quote Donald Trump:

'Many people are afraid to fail, so they don't try. They may dream, talk and even plan, but they don't take that critical step of putting their money and their effort on the line. To succeed in business, you must take risks. Even if you fail, that's how you learn. There has never been and will never be, an Olympic skater who didn't fall in the ice.'

I wish you great health, wealth and prosperity.

Abhishek Kumar